Teaching Kids

Of All Ages
To Ask Questions

Marilyn M. Toomey

Illustrated by Kevin Newman

98 97 96 95 TS 6 5 4 3 2 1

ISBN: 0-923573-18-6

Table of Contents

Preface

Teaching kids to ask questions is one of the unavoidable challenges of speech/language pathologists, special needs teachers and classroom teachers. I'm sure that others have had experiences similar to this — a successful language lesson is completed and a student looks at you and asks, "When I can go?"

This ego-deflating episode was repeated many times in my own experience as a speech/language pathologist. Each time, I wished for a resource with hundreds of items to help teach correct question forms. So, here it is -- a book offering hundreds of items to help *you* teach students of a wide age range to ask questions.

Asking questions, in our language, involves inverting word order in sentences, using specific question words and/or using a rising vocal inflection. Question-asking ability develops as language ability grows. As one becomes more proficient in language he or she is capable of formulating more complex questions. Elements of syntax and morphology such as the inversion rule and correct use of question words develop as part of a child's language system during preschool years.

This book is intended to help speech/language pathologists and teachers teach the elements of question formulation to children who have not acquired them as expected. Also, there is abundant material to help older students and adults who are learning English as a second language.

The book is divided into three sections. Section One targets young learners. Children learn vocabulary and rules of question formulation working through dozens of illustrated pages, each focusing on a specific syntactic element or elements. Section Two is included as a reference for speech/language pathologists and educators. This section presents reference material for selected rules of syntax which apply to question formulation. Section Three includes over 40 pages of exercises offering plenty of material for older students and adults improve their question-asking skills.

Kevin and I hope this book helps to make your lesson planing and teaching experiences more productive and pleasant, and, at times, even fun!

Marilyn

Introduction – Section 1

This section contains 48 pages of activities to help young language learners develop the ability to ask questions. Ranging from a very basic introduction to inverting words of a sentence to form a question to asking questions containing indirect objects, these pages present lessons in the language of questions.

The lessons are centered around the experiences of ten children. The same characters recur throughout this section stimulating questions of action, time, space, possession and other concepts. Young students should become familiar with these ten characters and motivated to follow them through the pages of this section.

Each page targets particular syntactic elements or words related to question formulation. A page-by-page instruction guide to the pages in Section One is presented on pp. 3 to 5. Each entry in this instruction guide corresponds to it's respective page or pages in Section One. These comments are intended to help you plan your lessons more effectively by clearly stating the goals of each page in this section.

Instruction Guide

*Each of the items explains the objectives of the
corresponding page or pages in Section One.*

Page 7   This is an illustration of changing word positions of a sentence to form a question. On some of the following pages students will use word cards to actually experience this inversion tactically and visually. This page can be used as a model for such activities.

Page 8   The children who will reappear throughout the first section of this book are introduced. Using the names of these children students will produce sentences (THIS IS ANN.) and rearrange the words to form questions (IS THIS ANN?).

Page 9   This exercise introduces the question word **who**.

Page 10   Here students are asked to write questions. The first word of each question is given at the beginning and the question mark is given at the end of each item.

Page 11   Here a progressive verb (**-ing** ending) plus auxiliary **is** describes the action of each of the children (Kim is running.) Students are to convert each of these statements on top of the page into a question beginning with **who** and each statement at the bottom of the page into a question beginning with **what**.

Page 12   This exercise requires students to manipulate word cards to construct sentences and corresponding questions. Students should construct and say a sentence, then rearrange the words and change the punctuation and ask a question. **Yes/no** answers to questions can also be presented and practiced in this way: Ask a student to select a picture card of a child doing something (i.e. Kim running) from a group of cards placed up-side-down on the table. Then ask her to select an action word card (i.e. **running**) in the same way. The student should look at the picture and form the question. If the picture and word cards match the answer is **yes**, if not the answer is **no**.

Page 13   Here students write questions to find out what someone is doing or who is doing something.

Page 14   Here students are introduced to the plural verb **are** and the plural pronoun **they**. The instructions tell the students to write the question, "What are they doing?" Prior to completing this page, instruction and modeling of plural vs. singular verbs and pronouns and verb and pronoun agreement should be done.

Page 15   This exercise introduces questions that are answered using transitive verbs and direct objects (i.e. Maria is wearing a crown.) The student is now dealing with more information. Notice that the two children wearing the same kind of hat follow each other in the lists. You might add some extra challenges by instructing students to ask, "Who is wearing a _____ hat?" and, "Who else is wearing a (same ___) hat?" Also, students can practice asking/answering questions using the plural verb form **are** and the plural pronoun **they** (i.e. Ann and Ken are wearing the same thing. What are they wearing?)

3

Page 16 Students here will write questions corresponding to statements attending to singular/plural verbs/pronouns. Noun/pronoun relationships can be illustrated by asking students to do this page twice, once using childrens names, once using correct pronouns.

Page 17-18 Page 17 is much like page 14 where students ask and answer questions using present progressive verbs. On page 18 students use the word **has** in place of is holding. Correctly using the words **has** and **have** can be quite challenging.

Page 19 The question word **whose** is introduced.

Page 20 This page is intended to strengthen students' use of **have/has** in questions/statements. These pictures and words should be pasted on index cards. Students should select pictures, then ask and answer questions using the word cards. Encourage such questions/answers as, "What do you have?"/"I have a ____."; "What does (a student's name) have?"/"He has a ____."; "Who has a ____?" This activity can be repeated using many different pictures or objects.

Page 21 Students will contrast **has/have** in writing on this page.

Page 22-23 These activities are intended to develop students' ability to ask questions including both, subjective and objective pronouns (i.e. **she/her**, **he/his**). Mastering correct use of these pronouns is difficult for some students. Also these exercises provide good opportunities to strengthen the concept of right and left.

Page 24 This activity introduces the infinitive phrase, **to eat** as well as contrasting the progressive verb **is eating** and the simple present tense verb **(does) like**. These questions/statements should be modeled for students before they complete the exercise.

Page 25 Here students must carefully read statements and write questions as indicated.

Page 26-27 Students here can be creative in asking and answering questions to find out and share information about each other.

Page 28 This page introduces students to questions dealing with time. Students simply ask the question, "What time is it?" Other students can answer by saying, "It's (time)."

Page 29-31 Students practice asking questions to find out when events occur. Pages 29 and 30 require questions with singular, simple present tense verbs; page 31 plural present tense verbs. This contrast should be pointed out and carefully modeled for students.

Page 32 This page addresses holidays and focuses on the question, "When do we celebrate (holiday)?" For added interest include students' birthdays or other special events that occur each year at the same time.

Page 33 Students practice asking "when" questions requiring simple past tense verbs.

Page 34 Students ask "when" questions requiring simple future tense verbs.

Page 35 "Where" questions are introduced.

Page 36 Pretending to be movers working to deliver Mike's family's things to a new home, students ask questions using **where** plus **should**.

Page 37   Pretending to be Mike, students ask questions to find out where his things are. Note the contrast between questions requiring singular and plural (**is/are**) verbs.

Page 38   Students are asked to write questions asking where something is. The example shows the question in the first person indicating that students are asking questions from the pictured child's point of view. This should be pointed out. Note, the last item on this page requires the plural verb **are** and pronoun **our**.

Page 39   "Why" questions are introduced. Students ask why each of the children needs the thing that she or he is holding. Encourage students to think of good reasons why, and state the reasons answering each other's questions.

Page 40   Students ask why each of these professionals need the items listed beside each picture.

Page 41   Students practice asking "why" questions using simple present tense verbs.

Page 42   This page is much like the preceding page, but the questions require simple past tense verbs.

Page 43   This activity contrasts asking questions about events that will take place in the future and asking questions about the same events after they have taken place. Careful modeling should be done for students so they can hear this difference.

Page 44   "How" questions are introduced.

Page 45   Students practice a variety of questions as the pretend to ask about John's family's camping trip.

Page 46   Students practice asking a variety of question using the modal auxiliary **should**.

Page 47   Students practice asking questions using modals **can** and **can't** and the phrase **would like to** as they role-play Kim and her mother.

Page 48   Students practice asking questions using the phrase **supposed to**. This is a frequently occurring phrase and is worth the time to practice for improved pronunciation as well as sentence/question formulation.

Page 49   Students practice asking and answering questions about where animals live.

Page 50   "Which" questions are introduced.

Page 51   Students practice asking "which" questions pretending to be Ken asking his cousin which of two things he likes better.

Page 52   Here students ask questions containing indirect objects.

Page 53   Here students will ask why one of the children gave his or her object or objects to another child. Students should be encouraged to use imagination and give answers beginning with **maybe**, indicating probability.

Page 54   This page was included as a review of question words or perhaps to be used for classroom display. Or, here's an idea! Have students make "question books" using some of the pages in Section One. This page could be used for a take-home question practice book.

To ask a question change the words of a **sentence** around like this...

HERE IS JOHN.

IS JOHN HERE?

This is an activity allowing students to experience rearranging words of a sentence to form a question. The pictures of children, children's names, punctuation marks and words should be pasted on separate cards. Guide students to construct sentences by arranging the cards, then rearrange the cards and change the punctuation to form questions as shown in the example at the bottom of the page.

THIS IS . ?
KIM MIKE BRENDA
JULIE ANN MARIA
KEN LEE JEFF JOHN

Example:

| THIS | IS | JULIE | . |

| IS | THIS | JULIE | ? |

To ask some questions use the question word **who**. Ask a question with the word **who** to find out who each child is. Answer each question.

Example:

Who is this?

This is Kim.

Who ....?

.... **Ann.**

Who ....?

.... **John.**

Who ....?

.... **Maria.**

Who ....?

.... **Julie.**

Who ....?

.... **Ken.**

Who ....?

.... **Lee.**

Who ....?

.... **Jeff.**

Who ....?

.... **Mike.**

Who ....?

.... **Brenda.**

Write a question for each of these answers.

This is John.

Is_____?

This is Lee.

Is_____?

This is Ann.

Is_____?

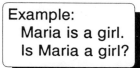

John is a boy.

Is_____?

Lee is a boy.

Is_____?

Ann is a girl.

Is_____?

Look at these pictures. Each child is doing something.

> Ask a question about **who** is doing each of these things. Each question should begin with **Who**.

1. Kim is running.   *Example:* **Who** is running?
2. Lee is jumping.
3. Mike is sitting.
4. John is hopping.
5. Maria is walking.
6. Julie is running.
7. Brenda is jumping.
8. Ann is sitting.
9. Jeff is hopping.
10. Ken is walking.

Mike

Lee

Ken

Kim

Brenda

> Ask a question about **what** each of these children is doing. Each question should begin with **What**.

1. Kim is running.   *Example:* **What** is Kim doing?
2. Lee is jumping.
3. Mike is sitting.
4. John is hopping.
5. Maria is walking.
6. Julie is running.
7. Brenda is jumping.
8. Ann is sitting.
9. Jeff is hopping.
10. Ken is walking.

Jeff

Ann

Julie

John

Maria

11

This is an activity allowing students to experience rearranging words of a sentence to form a question. The pictures of children, children's names, punctuation marks and words should be pasted on separate cards. Guide students to construct sentences by arranging the cards, then rearrange the cards and change the punctuation to form questions as shown in the example at the bottom of the page.

Jeff hopping

Brenda jumping

Julie running

Mike sitting

Ken walking

IS   YES   NO   .   ?
KEN   MIKE   BRENDA
JULIE   JEFF   HOPPING
JUMPING   SITTING
WALKING   RUNNING

Example:

 Julie running

| IS | JULIE | RUNNING | ? |

 Julie running

| YES | . |

Pretend like you want to know what each of these children is doing. Write a question for each of these answers. Begin your questions with the word **What**.

Ken is walking.

_____ **?**

Lee is jumping.

_____ **?**

Ann is sitting.

_____ **?**

Pretend like you want to know who is doing each of these things. Write a question for each of these answers. Begin your questions with the word **Who**.

Brenda is jumping.

_____ **?**

Kim is running.

John is hopping.

_____ **?**   _____ **?**

Look at the pictures of children. The two children in each picture are doing the same thing. Pretend that you want to know **what** the children in each picture are doing. Write your question.

Example:
    Maria and Ken are walking.
    What are they doing?

Lee and Brenda are jumping.

_____ **?**

Mike and Ann are sitting.

_____ **?**

Kim and Julie are running.

_____ **?**

Jeff and John are hopping.

_____ **?**

Look at these pictures. Each child is wearing a hat.

Ask a question to find out **who** is wearing each hat. Each question should begin with **Who**.

Ann

1. Mike is wearing a sailor hat.
   Example: **Who** is wearing a sailor hat?

Mike

2. Julie is wearing a sailor hat.
3. Ken is wearing a chef's hat.
4. Ann is wearing a chef's hat.
5. Lee is wearing a cowboy hat.
6. Brenda is wearing a cowboy hat.
7. Jeff is wearing a police hat.
8. Kim is wearing a police hat.
9. John is wearing a crown.
10. Maria is wearing a crown.

Jeff

Lee

John

Ask a question to find out **what** each child is wearing. Each question should begin with **What**.

1. Mike is wearing a sailor hat.
   Example: **What** is Mike wearing?

2. Julie is wearing a sailor hat.
3. Ken is wearing a chef's hat.
4. Ann is wearing a chef's hat.
5. Lee is wearing a cowboy hat.
6. Brenda is wearing a cowboy hat.
7. Jeff is wearing a police hat.
8. Kim is wearing a police hat.
9. John is wearing a crown.
10. Maria is wearing a crown.

Brenda

Ken

Maria

Kim

Julie

Pretend like you want to know what each child **is** wearing. Write a question for each of these answers.

 **Maria is wearing a crown.**

_____?

Ann is wearing a chef's hat.

_____?

 **Kim is wearing a police hat.**

_____?

Ken is wearing a chef's hat.

_____?

 **Lee is wearing a cowboy hat.**

_____?

Pretend like you want to know what these children **are** wearing. Write a question for each of these answers.

Kim and Jeff are wearing police hats.

_____?

 **Maria and John are wearing crowns.**

_____?

16

Look at these pictures. Each child is holding something.

**Ask a question about *who* is holding something.
Each question should begin with *Who*.**

John

1. Mike is holding a fishing pole.
    Example: **Who** is holding a fishing pole.

2. Maria is holding a baseball and baseball bat.
3. Julie is holding knitting needles and yarn.
4. Ken is holding a soccer ball.
5. John is holding a tennis racquet and ball.
6. Lee is holding a radio.
7. Brenda is holding a hammer and some wood.
8. Jeff is holding paints and a brush.
9. Ann is holding seeds and a flower pot.
10. Kim is holding ice skates.

Mike

Ann

**Think about *what* each of the children has. Ask
your partner questions about what each child is
holding. Each question should begin with *What*.**

Kim

1. Mike is holding a fishing pole.
    Example: **What** is Mike holding?

2. Maria is holding a baseball and baseball bat.
3. Julie is holding knitting needles and yarn.
4. Ken is holding a soccer ball.
5. John is holding a tennis racquet and ball.
6. Lee is holding a radio.
7. Brenda is holding a hammer and some wood.
8. Jeff is holding paints and
    a brush.
9. Ann is holding seeds and
    a flower pot.
10. Kim is holding ice skates.

Jeff

Lee

Ken

Maria

Julie

Brenda

Ann Julie Brenda Ken Jeff Kim Lee Mike

John

Think about what each child has. Look at the objects at the bottom of the page. Draw a line from each object to the child who should have the object. The pictures on the top of the page will help you. Ask a question to find out **what** each child has.

Example:
  What does Jeff have?
  Jeff has paints.

Maria

Look at the pictures on the top of the page. The children are holding their things or wearing their hats. Look at the pictures below showing only the objects and hats. Ask a question to find out whose object or hat is pictured.

1.

2.

3.

4.

5.

6.

7.

8.

9.

10.

Write a question for each answer below.
Begin each question with whose.

1. This is kim's hat.

 _____ ?

2. This is Maria's bat.

 _____ ?

3. This is Ann's plant.

_____ ?

4. This is Lee's radio.

 _____ ?

Have fun asking questions. You and your partner should cut out these pictures and paste them onto cards.
Part 1. Choose one of the pictures and tell your partner what you have. Your partner should choose a picture and you should ask him what he has.
Part 2. Others in the group should choose pictures and you can take turns asking them what each of them has. Also, ask your partner what someone else has.

Use these words and learn about the words we use to ask questions. Your teacher will help you learn how words make sentences and how they make questions.

I HAVE A . ?

WHAT DO YOU HAS

SHE HE WHO DOES

Write a question and a sentence for each of these pictures. The question will ask **what** the child has. The sentence will answer the question telling what the child has.

What_____ ?

Mike_____ .

What_____ ?

Jeff_____ .

What_____ ?

Julie_____ .

What_____ ?

Lee_____ .

What_____ ?

Maria_____ .

Look at Maria. She has many things in her **right** hand and many more things in her **left** hand. Ask your partner what Maria has in her hands.

Pretend like you want to know:

1. what Maria has in her right hand,
2. what else she has in her right hand,
3. what Maria has in her left hand,
4. what else she has in her left hand.

22

Look at Jeff. He has many things in his **right** hand and
many more things in his **left** hand. Ask your partner
what Jeff has in his hands.

Pretend like you want to know:

1. what Jeff has in his right hand,

2. what else he has in his right hand,

3. what Jeff has in his left hand,

4. what else he has in his left hand.

23

Jeff Ann Ken Mike Kim
Maria John Julie Lee Brenda

Each child is eating something that he or she likes to eat. Look at the pictures of children near the top of this page to see what the children are eating. Draw a line from the picture of each child below to something she or he likes to eat.

Ask questions to find out:
what each child is eating,
who is eating each food,
what each likes to eat,
who likes to eat each food.

Example:
What is Brenda eating?
Who is eating a hot dog?
What does Brenda like to eat?
Who likes to eat hot dogs?

Read the instructions for each of the exercises below. Write a question.

1. Someone is eating an apple. You want to know **who**.

Mike

_____ ?

2. Someone is eating pizza. You want to know **who**.

Ann

_____ ?

3. John is eating something. You want to know **what**.

_____ ?

4. Julie and Ken are eating something. You want to know **what**.

_____ ?

5. Brenda and Jeff are eating something. You want to know **what**.

_____ ?

6. Someone likes to eat spaghetti. You want to know **who**.

_____ ?

Kim

7. Lee and Ann like to eat something. You want to know **what**.

_____ ?

Practice asking questions about what your friends like to eat and other things that they like to do.

Example:
You want to know what someone likes to ride.
What do you like to ride?

1. You want to know what someone likes to eat.

2. You want to know what someone likes to drink.

3. You want to know what someone likes to wear.

4. You want to know what someone likes to play.

5. You want to know what someone likes to listen to.

6. You want to know what someone likes to sit on.

7. You want to know what someone likes to watch on TV.

8. You want to know where someone likes to go on vacation.

9. You want to know what someone likes to draw.

10. You want to know what someone likes to pretend.

Use your imagination. Pretend like you just got a new pen pal. Write a letter to your pen pal asking questions so that you can get to know him or her. Ask him or her what he or she likes to:

play	read	wear
eat	watch on TV	talk about.

Dear_____

I'm happy to be your pen pal. I'd like to ask you some questions so I can learn about you. _____

_____

_____

_____

_____

_____

_____

_____

_____

_____

_____

Your pen pal,

_____

Ask questions about time. Ask your partner what time it is for some of these clocks. Take turns so that your partner can also ask you what time it is on some of the other clocks.

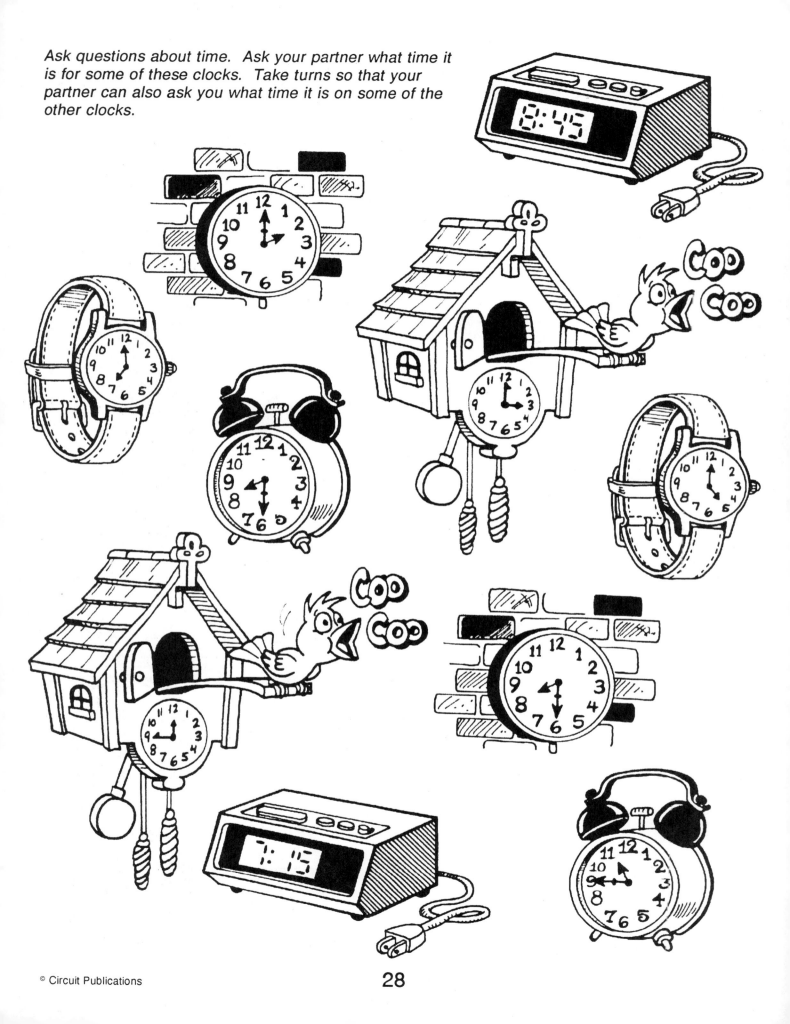

28

Think about things that you do at different times during the day. Look at the boxes. In each box you see a picture of a child and a picture of a clock.. The time on the clock tells the time at which the child does something each day. What he or she does is printed at the bottom of the box.

*Pretend like you want to know **when** each child does something each day. Ask a question about each one. Your partner should answer.*

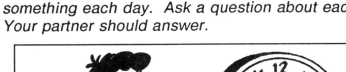

Example:
  Mike eats lunch...
  When does Mike eat lunch?
  Mike eats lunch at 12:00 o'clock.

  Maria wakes up

 Jeff goes to school

  Mike eats lunch

 Brenda has recess

  Lee eats breakfast

  Ann comes home from school

  John sets the table

 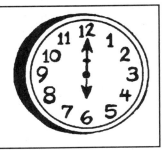 Ken eats dinner

  Julie eats lunch

  Kim watches TV

29

*Practice asking questions to find out **when** each of the children usually do special things. Your partner should answer your questions.*

Example:
When does Mike have baseball practice?
Mike has baseball practice on Monday.

Monday

Mike — baseball practice

Tuesday

Lee — piano lesson

Wednesday

Maria — mows lawn

Thursday

Ken — hockey practice

Friday

Brenda — shopping with mom

Saturday

Kim — helps dad wash car

Sunday

Ann — visits grandpa and grandma

*Write a question for each answer below. Begin your question with **When**.*

1. Lee has a piano lesson on Tuesday.

_____ **?**

2. Maria mows the lawn on Wednesday.

_____ **?**

3. Ken has hockey practice on Thursday.

_____ **?**

*Practice asking questions to find out **when** these children do special things at school. Your partner should answer your questions.*

Monday

Maria   Julie 3   gym

Tuesday

computer

Lee   Jeff

Wednesday

John   Ann   library

Thursday

Kim   Ken   music

Friday

Mike   Brenda   art

*Write a question for each answer below. Begin each question with **When**.*

1. Kim and Ken have music on Thursday.

_____ ?

2. Mike and Brenda have art on Friday.

_____ ?

3. John and Ann go to the library on Wednesday

_____ ?

4. Lee and Jeff use the computer on Tuesday.

_____ ?

5. Maria and Julie go to gym on Monday.

_____ ?

We celebrate different holidays at different times of the year.
Below is a list of the months of the year with a picture
representing a holiday celebrated on a day during that month.

January	February	March	April
New Years Day Martin Luther King Day	Valentine's Day Presidents' Day	St. Patrick's Day	Passover Easter Sunday
May	June	July	August
Mothers' Day Memorial Day	Fathers' Day Flag Day	American Independence Day	Summer Fun
September	October	November	December
Labor Day 1st day of school	Holloween	Thanksgiving	Christmas Chanukah Kwanzaa

Ask a question as if you want to know **when** we celebrate
each of these holidays. Begin your question with the word
when. Your partner should answer you, telling you during
which month we celebrate the holiday that you asked about.

1. Halloween
2. Mothers' Day
3. Chanukah
4. Valentine's Day
5. Memorial Day
6. Fathers' Day
7. Martin Luther King Day
8. Thanksgiving
9. Kwanzaa
10. Christmas
11. Labor Day
12. New Years Day
13. American Independence Day
14. St. Patrick's Day
15. Presidents' Day
16. return to school
17. Passover
18. your partner's birthday
19. Flag Day
20. Easter Sunday

*Each of these children did some things **last week** on the day that she or he was supposed to. Here are the things that each one did. Read each sentence. Change the sentence to a question asking when they **did** these things.*

Example:
    Mike went to baseball practice on Monday.
    When did Mike go to baseball practice?

1. Lee had a piano lesson on Tuesday.

2. Maria cut the grass on Wednesday.

3. Ken played hockey on Thursday.

4. Brenda went shopping with her mom on Friday.

5. Kim helped her dad wash their car on Saturday.

6. Ann Visited her grandma and grandpa on Sunday.

7. Maria and Julie went to gym on Monday.

8. Lee and John had their computer class on Tuesday.

9. Ken and Brenda had music on Wednesday.

10. John and Ann went to the library on Wednesday.

11. Mike and Kim had art on Friday.

*These students have just returned to school from summer vacation. They expect to know when they will do some of the things that they hope to do. Ask the questions as these children would ask if they wanted to know **when** they **will** do each of these things.*

Example:
  get our books...
  "When will we get our books?"

1. have a spelling test
2. have a class party
3. put on a play
4. use the computer
5. go to the symphony
6. learn about electricity
7. plant seeds
8. write a class newsletter
9. go to the library
10. learn a new song
11. collect leaves
12. go to the zoo
13. see a movie
14. go to the Science Museum
15. do a science experiment
16. learn about insects
17. get our eyes checked
18. write poems
19. learn how robots work
20. see a ballet
21. have our pictures taken
22. make a sculpture out of clay
23. learn about dinosaurs
24. sign up for basketball tournaments

*Here is a picture of a closet with some things hanging on **hangers**, some things on the **shelf** and some things on the **floor**.*

*Ask questions as though you want to know **where** each of these things is.*
Your partner should answer your questions.

Example:
rain coat...
Where is the rain coat?
The rain coat is on a hanger.

jacket	ballet slippers
skirt	gloves
dress-up shoes	pants
shirt	sleeping bag
purse	baseball uniform
goggles	umbrella
cowboy boots	slippers
ear muffs	dress
hat	gym shoes
flippers	ice skates
bike helmet	roller blades

Mike's family is moving into their new house. The movers are busy taking things off of the moving van. They need to know **where** each of the things belong. The movers must ask Mike's family where they should put things.
Pretend like you are one of the movers. Ask Mike's family **where** you should put each of these things.

Example:
the lamp...
Where should I put the lamp?

1. the green table
2. the coffee pot
3. the red chair
4. the books
5. the radio
6. the piano
7. the fishing pole
8. the hammer
9. the gasoline can
10. the baseball and bat
11. the telescope
12. the electric drill
13. the grandfather clock
14. the bed
15. the night stand
16. the picnic basket
17. the pots and pans
18. the rolling pin
19. the toaster
20. the ax
21. the washing machine
22. the umbrellas

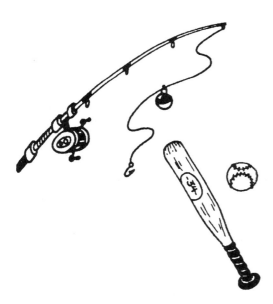

*Mike and his family have just finished moving into their new house. Everything has been brought into the house, but poor Mike can't find many of this things. Practice asking questions like Mike does as he asks **where** to find his things.*

1. kite
2. cowboy boots
3. math book
4. book bag
5. umbrella
6. calculator
7. notebook
8. basketball
9. shin guards
10. soccer ball
11. watch
12. flippers
13. Celtics sweat shirt
14. tool kit
15. sun glasses

16. fishing rod
17. remote control car
18. race track
19. new tube socks
20. pillow
21. blue jacket
22. checker game
23. bike helmet
24. alarm clock
25. slippers
26. radio
27. markers
28. library book
29. scrap book
30. baseball bat

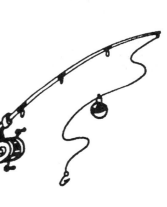

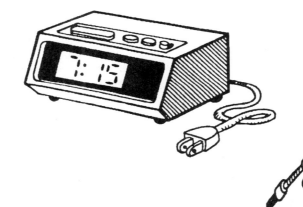

37

Each of the children wants to know **where** *something is. Help ask questions to find out.*

1. Jeff wants to know **where** his bat is.

_____?

2. Lee wants to know **where** his radio is.

_____?

3. Ann wants to know **where** her seeds are.

_____?

4. Kim wants to know **where** her ice skates are.

_____?

5. Ken wants to know **where** his soccer ball is.

_____?

6. Maria and John want to know **where** their crowns are.

_____?

38

Each of the children has something that she or he will use in order to do something. Pretend like you want to know **why** these children need these things. Ask a question to find out. Your partner should think, use her imagination, and try to answer your question.

Lee

Mike

Ann

Julie

John

Brenda

Kim

Maria

Ken

Jeff

Write a question for each of these answers. Begin each question with **Why**.

1. Ann needs seeds because she's going to plant flowers.

_____ **?**

2. Brenda needs a hammer and nails because she's going to build something.

_____ **?**

3. Jeff needs paints because he's going to paint a picture.

_____ **?**

*Pretend like you want to know **why** these workers need the tools listed beside their pictures.*

chalk
book
stars

microscope
test tube
computer

thermometer
bandage
stethoscope

Teacher

Scientist

Doctor

saw
hammer
nails

spoon
frying pan
oven

Carpenter

Chef

Every day Kim does things that will help her stay safe, clean, healthy and organized. Below, in the left hand column is a list of things that she does. In the right hand column is a list of reasons why she does these things.

*Pretend like you want to know **why** Kim does each of these things. Ask a question for each one. Then draw a line to the best reason you can find in the column on the right.*

> Example:
> Why does Kim brush her teeth?
> ...so she doesn't get cavities

brushes her teeth	so it will look nice and not be tangled
eats lots of fruit and vegetables	so she's ready to write her lessons at school
sharpens her pencil every morning	so they will grow
takes her dog for a walk after school	so they will look neat and not be wrinkled
waters her plants	so she won't be tired in school the next day
hangs up her clothes	so her body gets healthy foods
looks both ways before she crosses the street	so she is safe while riding in the car
wears a seat belt	so she can learn
brushes her hair	so she doesn't get cavities
is nice to everyone	so her dog gets exercise
puts her homework in her book bag each night	so she can tell if a car is coming
	so people will be nice to her
gets her clothes ready for school the next day before she goes to bed	so she's sure to have her homework the next day at school
saves her money to buy presents for her friends for their birthdays	so she can save time getting dressed in the morning
gets enough sleep each night	so she has enough money to buy nice presents
does her homework	

Last week John did many things at home and at school to make things better for himself, his friends, his mom and dad and his teachers.

Below, in the column on the left is a list of things that he did. In the column on the right is a list of reasons why he did each of these things. Pretend like you want to know **why** John did each of these things. Ask a question for each one. Then draw a line to the best reason you can find in the column on the right.

Example:
   Why did John put air in his bike tires?
   ...because they were flat

put air in his bike tires	so he could put his clothes away
cleaned his mirror	because his old one had a hole in it
went to the dentist	so he could see himself clearly
wrote a letter to his grandma	to let her know he was thinking of her
cleaned out his closet	because they were flat
took his coat to the dry cleaners	so he would get a good grade
got a new football	because his hair was too long
bought some goldfish food	so she could get her shots
went to the library	because his friend wasn't home
studied for his science test	so he could feed his pet fish
planted a tiny tree in his front yard	so it would grow big and make a shady place in the yard
helped his neighbor carry some boxes	because they were too heavy for one person to carry
put new books on shelves in his classroom	so he could borrow some books
got a haircut	so he could help his teacher
took his cat to the vet	so he could get his teeth cleaned
took care of his friend's dog	because it was dirty
learned how to play hockey	so he can try out for the hockey team

*Julie's cousin, Karen is going to have a birthday party next Saturday. Julie wants to know what **will** happen at the party, so she asks Karen some questions.*
Help Julie ask questions about the party. She wants to know.

1. what kind of cake Karen will have

2. if they will have chocolate ice cream

3. what the children will drink at the party

4. if they will play games outside

5. if they will have a cook out

6. if the children will win prizes for the games

*The day after the party Julie called Karen to find out what **did** happen at the party.*
Help Julie ask Karen questions. She want to know:

1. what kind of cake Karen had

2. if they had chocolate ice cream

3. what the children drank at the party

4. if they played games outside

5. if they had a cook out

6. if the children won prizes for the games

*John's family is planning a camping trip. John must find out **how** to do many things while they're camping. Help John ask questions so he can find out how to:*

Example:
...choose a camp site
How do you choose a campsite?

1. put up a tent
2. roll up a sleeping bag
3. set up a cot
4. build a camp fire
5. cook a hot dog on a campfire
6. toast a marshmallow
7. cook popcorn on a campfire

8. keep the food cold
9. keep the bugs away
10. catch a fish
11. hike in the woods without getting lost
12. put out a campfire
13. take down a tent
14. clean up a campsite

John's family went camping during spring vacation. When John came back to school after the camping trip, his friends wanted to know about the trip.

Help John's friends ask questions. Just for fun pretend that your partner is John! Your partner should answer the questions just as John would. John's friend wants to know:

Example:
  ...where John's family went camping
  Where did you go camping?

1. how they got there

2. how long it took to get there

3. how they chose their camp site

4. how they put up the tent

5. if they slept in sleeping bags

6. how they made a campfire

7. what they had to eat

8. how they kept their food cold

9. how they cooked their food

10. if they toasted marshmallows

11. if they went hiking

12. if they caught any fish

13. if they saw any wild animals

14. when they went to sleep each night

15. if they slept in a tent

16. how cold it was at night

17. what they ate for breakfast

18. how they took their tent down

19. if they took pictures

Jeff's older brother, Bob just got a job at a restaurant. He's ready to work hard and needs to know what he should do. He has many questions for his boss about the things he should do at work. Help Bob ask questions. Bob wants to know:

Example:
    ...when he should start work
    When should I start work?

1. what he should wear

2. how he should get the tables ready

3. if he should fill the mustard and ketchup jars

4. how he should greet the customers

5. where he should get the menus to give to the customers

6. how he should explain the "specials of the day"

7. how long he should let a customer read the menu before he takes an order

8. what he should use to write down customers' orders

9. how he should tell the chef what to prepare for the customers

10. how he should figure out a customer's bill

11. what he should do to help clean up after the restaurant closes

Use your imagination! Pretend like you just got a job in one of the following places. Your partner should pretend to be your boss. Ask questions about what you should do in your new job. Take turns asking questions and being the "boss" in these pretend jobs.

Example:
    a bakery...
    When should I take the bread out of the oven?

1. a pizza parlor

2. a TV station

3. a lumber yard

4. a farm

5. a car wash

6. a grocery store

7. a garden center

8. a furniture store

9. a pet shop

10. a ranch

11. a flower shop

12. a movie theatre

13. a video store

14. a circus

15. a museum

Kim has the chicken pox. She is uncomfortable and unhappy. There are many things that she can't do because she needs to stay in bed and rest so she will get well.
*Kim asks her mom **why** she **can't** do the things she enjoys. Help Kim ask these questions. Kim wants to know why she can't:*

Example:
...call my friends
Why can't I call my friends?

1. play basketball
2. go to the parade
3. go to baseball practice
4. go on a picnic
5. go skating
6. invite a friend over
7. practice her tap dancing
8. go shopping
9. go to a movie

*Kim's mom knows that Kim can't do these things because she must get some rest. Mom asks Kim if she **would like to** do some quiet things.*

Example:
...listen to music
Would you like to listen to music?

1. watch a video
2. draw a picture
3. write a letter
4. do a puzzle
5. play with her dolls
6. read a story
7. look at a magazine
8. watch TV
9. play a quiet game

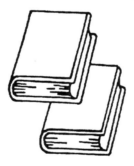

*Kim wonders **when** she **can** do some things that she can't do now. She wants to know when she can:*

Example:
...ride my bike
When can I ride my bike?

1. go hiking with her friends
2. go to the beach
3. have friends over
4. take her dog for a walk
5. go shopping
6. play tennis

47

Mike is going to a new school. He needs to know what he is **supposed to** *do at school, where things belong and when things happen. Help him ask questions so he can find out what is supposed to happen.*

Example:
...if he is supposed to write in his workbook
Am I supposed to write in my workbook?

1. where he is supposed to sit

2. where he is supposed to put his jacket

3. when he is supposed to meet the principal

4. when he is supposed to have a spelling test

5. if he is supposed to go to the library

6. if he is supposed to bring his books to computer class

7. when he is supposed to have lunch

8. when he is supposed to sharpen his pencil

9. where he is supposed to get his juice

10. if he is supposed to buy a lunch ticket

11. which door he is supposed to come in

12. if he is supposed to have a pencil box

13. how many pencils he is supposed to have

14. if he is supposed to take a note home

15. what kind of clothes he's supposed to have for gym class

16. if he's supposed to bring money in to pay for a class newspaper

Lee likes to learn about animals. He is reading about animals and the places where different animals live. Look at the pictures of animals in their homes. Ask a question to find out ***where*** *each animal lives. Your partner should answer your question.*

> Example:
> Where does a bird live?
> A bird lives in a nest.

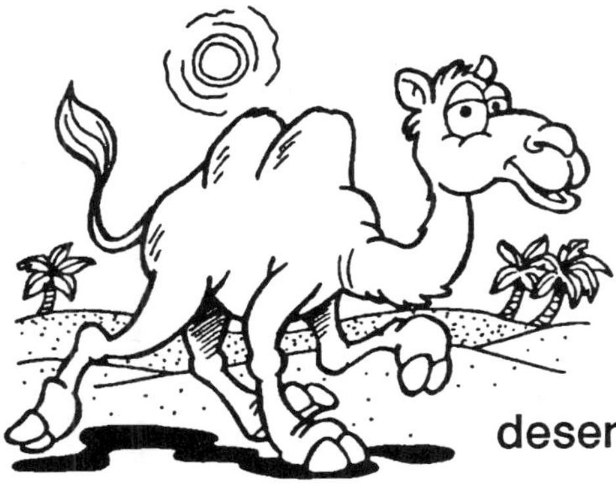

desert

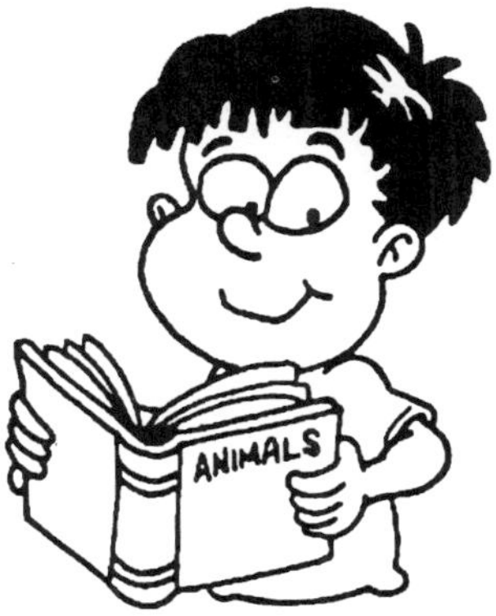

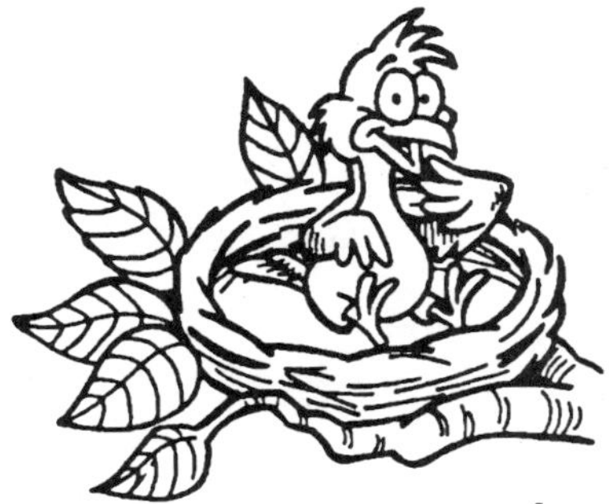

nest

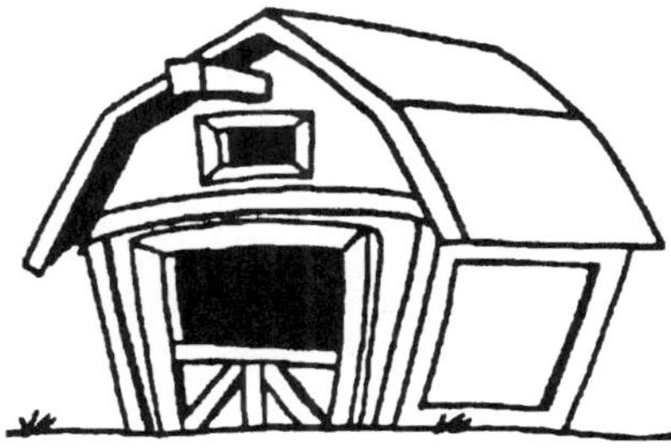

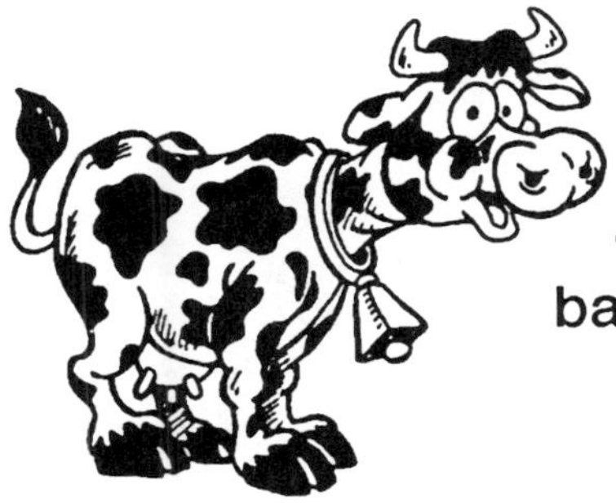

barn

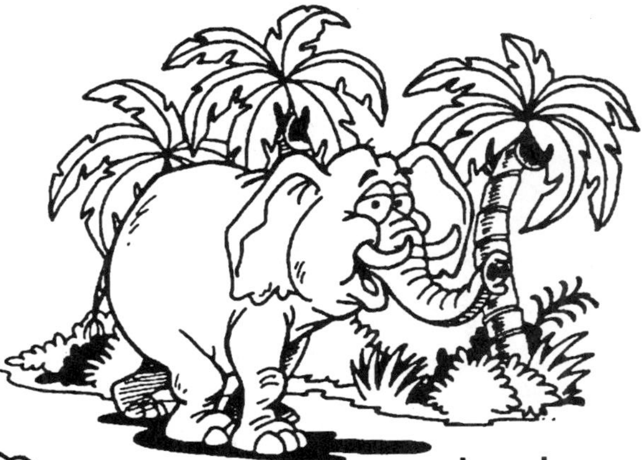

jungle

shell

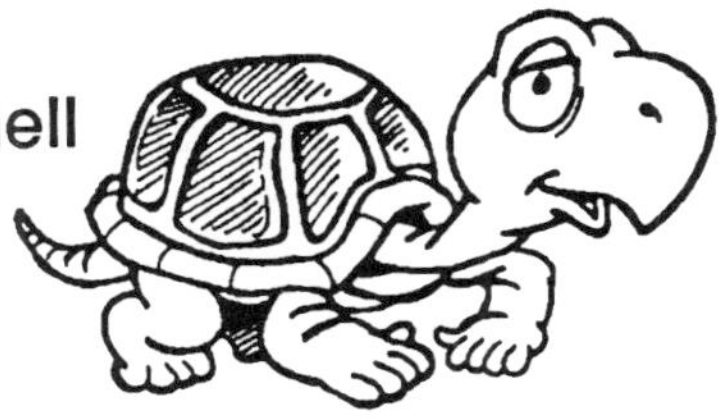

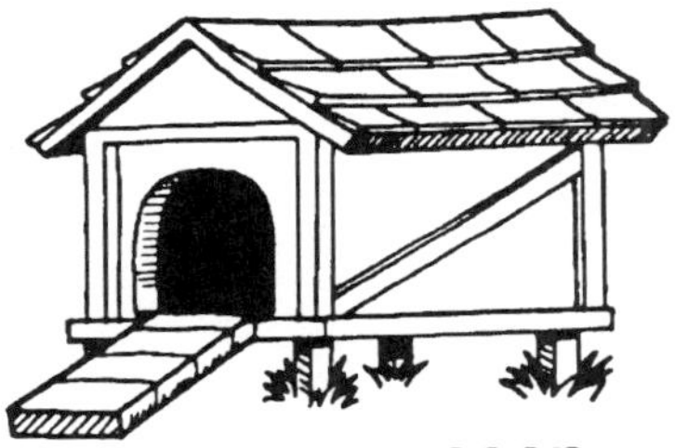

coop

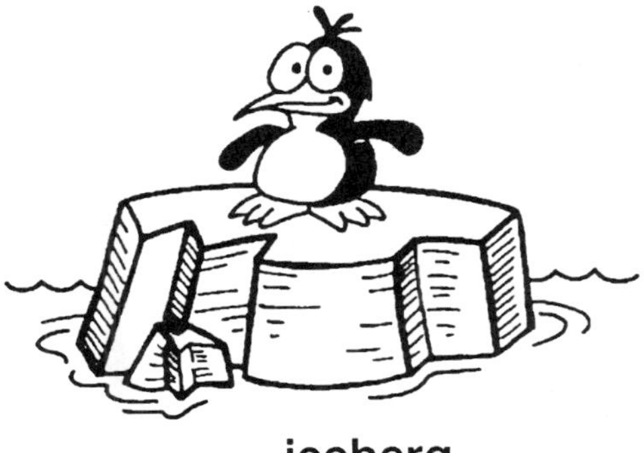

iceberg

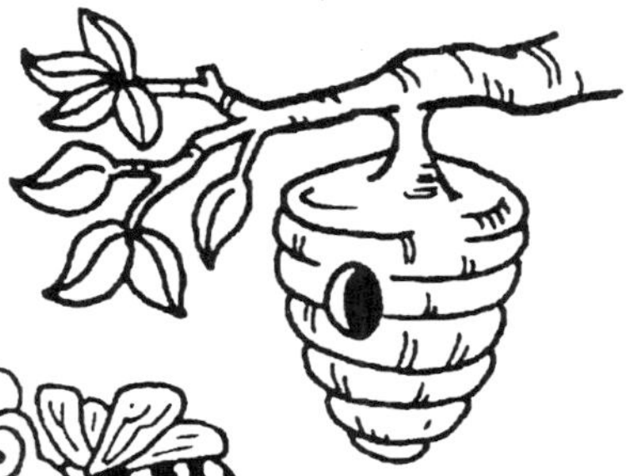

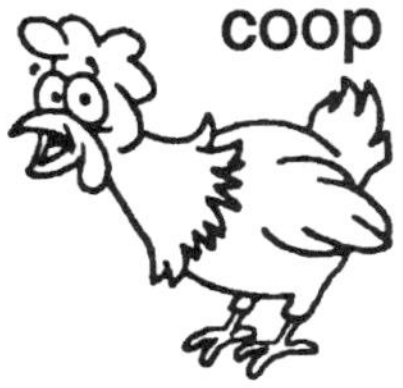

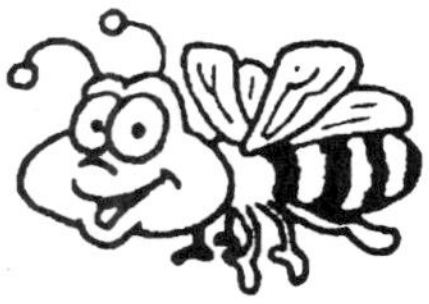

hive

web

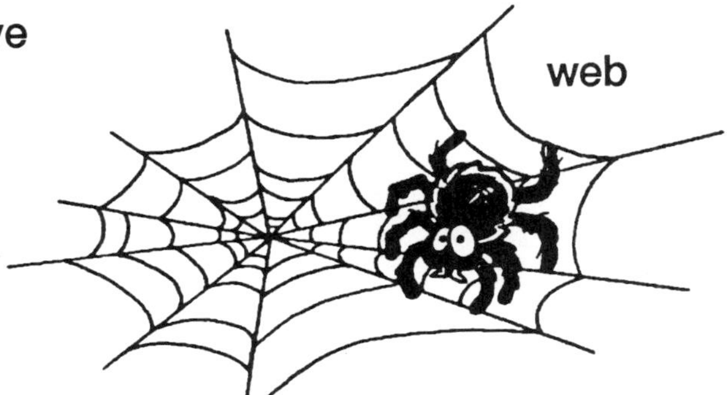

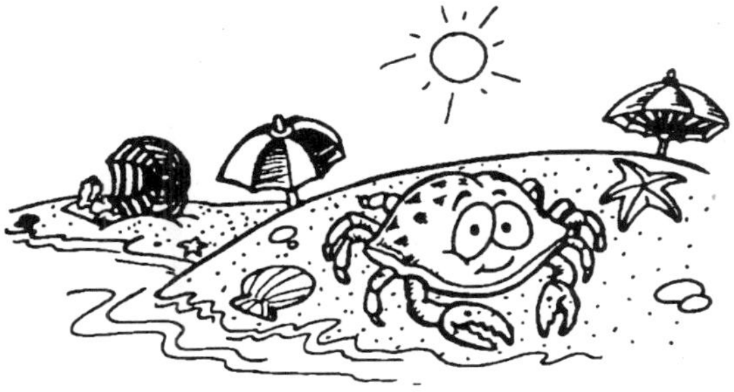

beach

Draw a line from the picture of the animal to the place where the animal lives. Ask **which** animal lives in each of these places. Your partner should answer your question.

Example:
Which animal lives in a nest?
A bird lives in a nest.

shell

beach

barn

hive

desert

nest

web

jungle

iceberg

coop

50

Ken's cousin is coming to visit. He will stay for a week.
Ken wants to make his cousin's visit special. He wants
to know what his cousin likes to do and to eat. Ken
thinks of things to ask his cousin.
He wants to know **which** one his cousin likes better.

Example:
fish or chicken...
Which do you like better,
fish or chicken?

1. pizza or tacos
2. hot dogs or hamburgers
3. lemonade or orange juice
4. ice cream or cake
5. popcorn or chips
6. apples or bananas
7. raisins or grapes
8. playing checkers or doing puzzles
9. drawing or painting picture
10. running races or playing tag
11. jumping rope or skating
12. riding bikes or hiking in the woods
13. listening to music or watching TV
14. building models or playing checkers
15. baking cookies or making pizza
16. shooting baskets or playing catch
17. football or soccer
18. going hiking or going to the beach
19. playing with race cars or radio controlled airplanes
20. building something real or making a model
21. watching videos or telling scary stories
22. sleeping on the top or bottom bunk

Look at the pictures below. Each child has something.

Look at the pictures below. All the things have been switched around! The children must have given their things to someone else.

Pretend like you want to know **who** gave something **to** one of the children. Ask questions so you can find out.
Example: Who gave the fishing pole to Julie?

Pretend like you want to know **what** each child gave **to** someone else. Ask questions so you can find out.
Example: What did Jeff give to Ann?

Who gave Brenda the Chicken Pox?

Ken

Jeff

John

Julie

Ann

Brenda

Why do you suppose Brenda gave the hammer to John? Maybe John needed it so he could do something.
*Think about **why** all the children gave their things to other children.*

Ask questions to find out. Your partner should use her imagination to answer your question telling you what she thinks.

Kim

Lee

Maria

Mike

Example:
  Why did Julie give her yarn to Jeff?
  Maybe Jeff needed the yarn so he could knit a scarf.

Why did Brenda get the chicken pox from Kim?

Remember the question words!

Introduction – Section 2

This section contains information for the professional in areas of syntax or morphology that apply to question formulation. The purpose of this section is to provide a speech/language pathologist or teacher with a means of discussing the elements of syntax or morphology with students' parents or educational associates and to assist in preparing individual education plans. Each of the pages in this section identifies and explains a particular syntactic element and, gives examples of sentences or questions when appropriate.

Below is a list of the items included in Section Two:

Simple past, present and future tense verbs

Regular and irregular verbs

Progressive present, past and future tense verbs

Perfect present, past and future tense verbs

Perfect progressive present, past and future tense verbs

Negative questions

Modal auxiliary verbs

Passive form of verbs

Reported speech or indirect discourse

Conditional statements

Tag questions

Question words

SIMPLE PAST, PRESENT AND FUTURE TENSE VERBS

Simple Present indicates that something was true in the past, is true in the present and will be true in the future. The simple present states facts or truths which occur as they are supposed to or to indicate routine, daily activity. In statements of simple present tense the subject occurs first and the simple form of the verb stands alone (preceding auxiliary *does* (singular) or *do* (plural), implied). In questions the subject/verb order is inverted auxiliary *does (do)* and the main verb are separated by the subject.

Simple Past indicates that something occurred at some time in the past; the event or action began and ended at a specific time in the past. In statements of simple past tense the simple past form of the main verb (-ed ending is added to the main verb or, in cases of irregular past tense verbs, the spelling of the verb is changed), the auxiliary *did* implied. In questions the subject/verb order is inverted, the preceding auxiliary *did* (singular), *do* (plural) and the main verb are separated by the subject.

Simple Future indicates that at a specific time in the future something will occur. In statements of simple future tense the subject occurs first. The main verb is preceded by the auxiliary *will* or the phrase *going to* plus a form of the verb *be*. In questions the subject/verb order is inverted, the main verb and the auxiliary *will* are separated by the subject. Or, an auxiliary form of *be* is separated by the subject from the phrase *going to* plus the main verb.

Simple Present Tense Statements
I (do) walk.
We (do) walk.
You (do) walk.
He walks (does walk).
They walk (do walk).

Simple Present Tense Questions
Do I walk?
Do we Walk?
Do you walk?
Does she walk?
Do they walk?

Simple Past Tense Statements
I walked (did walk).
We walked (did walk).
You walked (did walk).
It walked (did walk).
They walked (did walk).

Simple Past Tense Questions
Did I walk?
Did we walk?
Did you walk?
Did she walk?
Did they walk?

Simple Future Tense Statements
I will walk. I am going to walk.
We will walk. We are going to walk.
You will walk. You are going to walk.
He will walk. He is going to walk.
They will walk. They are going to walk.

Simple Future Tense Questions
Will I walk? Am I going to walk?
Will we walk? Are we going to walk?
Will you walk? Are you going to walk?
Will she walk? Is she going to walk?
Will they walk? Are they going to walk?

REGULAR VERBS

Here is a list of regular verbs. When the past tense is indicated,
an *-ed* ending is added to the simple form of the verb. If
the verb is spelled with an *-e* at the end, just add *-d*.

Simple Form	Simple Past Form	Simple Form	Simple Past Form
bake	baked	pass	passed
bark	barked	pat	patted
bat	batted	play	played
brush	brushed	polish	polished
buckle	buckled	pull	pulled
button	buttoned	push	pushed
clean	cleaned	rake	raked
climb	climbed	reach	reached
close	closed	rinse	rinsed
color	colored	rub	rubbed
comb	combed	scoop	scooped
cook	cooked	scrub	scrubbed
cover	covered	settle	settled
dust	dusted	skip	skipped
hop	hopped	stay	stayed
jump	jumped	stop	stopped
lock	locked	talk	talked
look	looked	tie	tied
mark	marked	treat	treated
mash	mashed	turn	turned
match	matched	wait	waited
melt	melted	walk	walked
mix	mixed	wash	washed
mop	mopped	watch	watched
open	opened	water	watered
paint	painted	wipe	wiped
park	parked	wish	wished

IRREGULAR VERBS

Here is a list of irregular verbs. These verbs do not take an *-ed* ending. Rather, they might require changes in spelling or no past tense marker at all when the past tense is indicated. The simple, simple past and past participle forms are given.

Simple Form	Simple Past Form	Past Participle Form	Simple Form	Simple Past Form	Past Participle Form
be	was, were	been	get	got	gotten
become	became	become	give	gave	given
begin	began	begun	go	went	gone
bite	bit	bitten	grow	grew	grown
bleed	bled	bled	have	had	had
blow	blew	blown	hear	heard	heard
break	broke	broken	hold	held	held
bring	brought	brought	keep	kept	kept
build	built	built	know	knew	known
burst	burst	burst	leave	left	left
buy	bought	bought	make	made	made
catch	caught	caught	pay	paid	paid
choose	chose	chosen	read	read	read
come	came	come	ride	rode	ridden
cost	cost	cost	ring	rang	rung
cut	cut	cut	rise	rose	risen
dig	dug	dug	run	ran	run
do	did	done	say	said	said
draw	drew	drawn	see	saw	seen
eat	ate	eaten	sell	sold	sold
fall	fell	fallen	sing	sang	sung
feel	felt	felt	slide	slid	slid
find	found	found	speak	spoke	spoken
fly	flew	flown	stand	stood	stood
forget	forgot	forgotten	steal	stole	stolen
freeze	froze	frozen	take	took	taken

PROGRESSIVE PRESENT, PAST and FUTURE TENSE VERBS

Present Progressive indicates that an action or event began in the past, is in progress at present and will likely continue into the future. In statements of present progressive the subject precedes the verb. The main verb (present pariciple) (-ing ending) is preceded by *is* or *are* (plural). In questions of present progressive, the subject/verb order is inverted, the main (present progressive form) and auxiliary verbs are separated by the subject.

Present Progressive Tense Statements
I am walking.
We are walking.
You are walking.
She is walking.
They are walking.

Present Progressive Tense Questions
Am I walking?
Are we walking?
Are you walking?
Is she walking?
Are they walking?

Past Progressive indicates that an action or event began in the past and was in progress at a specific moment in the past. In statements of past progressive the subject precedes the verb. The main verb (present participle form) is preceded by the auxiliary *was* or *were* (plural) . In questions of past progressive the subject/verb order is inverted, the main and auxiliary verbs are separated by the subject.

Past Progressive Statements
I was walking.
We were walking.
You were walking.
He was walking.
They were walking.

Past Progressive Questions
Was I walking?
Were we walking?
Were you walking?
Was he walking?
Were they walking?

Future Progressive indicates that an action or event will be in progress at a particular time in the future. In statements of future progressive the subject precedes the verb. The main verb (present progressive) is preceded by the auxiliaries *will* and *be*. The main verb might also be preceded by the progressive form of *be* where the phrase *be going to* occurs instead of *will*. In questions of future progressive the subject/verb order is inverted, the main verb separated from auxiliary verb or verb phrase by the subject.

Future Progressive Tense Statements
I will be walking. I am going to be walking.
We will be walking. We are going to be walking.
You will be walking. You are going to be walking.
He will be walking. He is going to be walking.
They will be walking. They are going to be walking.

Future Progressive Tense Questions
Will I be walking? Am I going to be walking?
Will we be walking? Are we going to be walking?
Will you be walking? Are you going to be walking?
Will he be walking? Is he going to be walking?
Will they be walking? Are they going to be walking?

PERFECT PRESENT, PAST and FUTURE TENSE VERBS

Present Perfect verbs indicate that something happened before now, at an indefinite time in the past; the specific time at which the action or event happened is not important. Also, using the adverb *since* this verb form indicates that an action or event began in the past and continues to the present. Statements of present perfect are formed with the subject preceding the verb. The past participle form of the verb is preceded by the auxiliary *has* or *have* (plural). Questions of present perfect are formed by inverting the subject/verb order. The main and auxiliary verbs are separated by the subject.

Present Perfect Tense Statements
I have walked.
We have walked.
You have walked
She has walked.
They have walked.

Present Perfect Tense Questions:
Have I walked?
Have we walked?
Have you walked?
Has she walked?
Have they walked?

Past Perfect indicates that an action or event was completed before another action or event occurred or before another time in the past. Statements of past perfect are formed with the subject preceding the verb. The past participle form of the verb is preceded by the auxiliary *had*. Questions of past perfect verbs are formed by inverting subject/verb order. The main and auxiliary verbs are separated by the subject.

Past Perfect Tense Statements
I had walked.
We had walked.
You had walked.
She had walked.
They had walked.

Past Perfect Tense Questions
Had I walked?
Had we walked?
Had you walked?
Had it walked?
Had they walked?

Future Perfect indicates that an activity will be completed before another time or event in the future. Statements of future perfect are formed with the subject preceding the verb. The past participle of the main verb is preceded by auxiliary verbs *will* and *have* and the past participle form of the verb *be (been)*. Questions of future perfect are formed by inverting the subject/verb order. The auxiliary *will* is separated from the remainder of the verb phrase by the subject.

Future Perfect Tense Statements
I will have been walking.
We will have been walking.
You will have been walking.
She will have been walking.
They will have been walking

Future Perfect Tense Questions
Will I have been walking?
Will we have been walking?
Will you have been walking?
Will he have been walking?
Will they have been walking?

PERFECT PROGRESSIVE PRESENT, PAST AND FUTURE TENSE VERBS

Present Perfect Progressive indicates the duration of an activity or event that began in the past and continues into the present. Adverbs and adverb phrases stating time concepts occur in such statements. Also, this verb form expresses an activity in progress in the recent past. Statements of present perfect progressive are formed with the subject preceding the verb. The main verb (progressive form) is preceded by the auxiliary *have* and the past participle of *be (been)*. Questions of present perfect progressive are formed by inverting the subject/verb order. The auxiliary *has* or *have* is separated from the remainder of the verb phrase by the subject.

Present Perfect Progressive Verb Statements
I have been walking.
We have been walking.
You have been walking
She has been walking.
They have been walking.

Present Perfect Progressive Verb Questions
Have I been walking?
Have we been walking?
Have you been walking?
Has he been walking?
Have they been walking?

Past Perfect Progressive indicates the length of time of an activity or event that was in progress prior to another activity or time in the past. This verb tense is also used to indicate an activity in progress in the recent past in relation to another time or activity. Statements of past perfect progressive are formed by the subject preceding the verb. The verb includes the auxiliary *had* and the past progressive form of the verb *be (been)* preceding the the present participle form of the main verb. Questions of past perfect progressive are formed by inverting subject/verb order. The auxiliary verb *had* is separated from the remainder of the verb phrase by the subject

Past Perfect Progressive Verb Statements
I had been walking.
We had been walking.
You had been walking.
It had been walking.
They had been walking,

Past Perfect Progressive Verb Questions
Had I been walking?
Had We been walking?
Had you been walking?
Had it been walking?
Had they been walking?

Future Perfect Progressive states the duration of an activity or event that will be in progress prior to the time of another event or before another time in the future. Statements of future perfect progressive are formed by the subject preceding the verb. The auxiliaries *will* and *have* precede the present participle form of *be (been)* and the present participle form of the main verb. Questions of future perfect progressive are formed by inverting subject/verb order. The auxiliary *will* is separated form the remainder of the verb phrase by the subject.

Future Perfect Progressive Verb Statements
I will have been walking.
We will have been walking.
You will have been walking.
She will have been walking.
They will have been walking.

Future Perfect Progressive Verb Questions
Will I have been walking?
Will we have been walking?
Will you have been walking?
Will he have been walking?
Will they have been walking?

NEGATIVE QUESTIONS

Negative questions communicate a speaker's belief as to whether something is or is not true. A form of the verb *be* or *do* occurs with *not,* usually in the form of a contraction and separated from the main verb by the subject.

Negative question (be)	*Negative question (do)*
Aren't I ready?	*Don't I have a ticket?*
Aren't you ready?	*Don't you have a ticket?*
Isn't he ready?	*Doesn't he have a ticket?*
Aren't we ready?	*Don't we have a ticket?*
Aren't you ready?	*Don't you have a ticket?*
Aren't they ready?	*Don't they have a ticket?*
Wasn't I ready?	*Didn't I have a ticket?*
Weren't you ready?	*Didn't you have a ticket?*
Wasn't she ready?	*Didn't he have a ticket?*
Weren't we ready?	*Didn't we have a ticket?*
Weren't you ready?	*Didn't you have a ticket?*
Weren't they ready?	*Didn't they have a ticket?*
Won't I be ready?	*Won't I have a ticket?*
Won't you be ready?	*Won't you have a ticket?*
Won't she be ready?	*Won't she have a ticket?*
Won't we be ready?	*Won't we have a ticket?*
Won't you be ready?	*Won't you have a ticket?*
Won't they be ready?	*Won't they have a ticket?*

MODAL AUXILIARY VERBS

Modal auxiliary verbs accompany main verbs in sentences. These auxiliary verbs serve to express a speaker's attitudes or feelings regarding necessity, probability, preference, expectation or permission.

Auxiliary verbs and similar words or phrases precede main verbs in sentences. In questions they are separated from main verbs by the subject of the sentence.

AUXILIARY VERBS THAT INDICATE DEGREES OF PROBABILITY OR NECESSITY

Statements

might	Your book might be in my locker.
should	Bikers should wear helmets.
could	This could be the last train in to town today.
ought	She ought to know about that.
can	Mario can windsurf.
going to	Charleen is going to sell her car.
will	Our band will march in the parade.
have got to	Ben has got to take his medicine each morning.
must	We must wear seatbelts .
supposed to	I am supposed to get paid on Friday.
able to	Margret is able to understand Chinese.

Questions

might	Might your book be in my locker?
should	Should bikers wear helmets?
could	Could this be the last train in to town today?
	(ought is not often used in simple questions)
can	Can Mario windsurf?
going to	Is Charleen going to sell her car?
will	Will our band march in the parade?
have got to	Has Ben got to take his medicine each morning?
must	Must we wear seatbelts?
supposed to	Am I supposed to get paid on Friday?
able to	Is Margret able to understand Chinese?

AUXILIARY VERBS AND SIMILAR WORDS THAT CONVEY REQUESTS OF PERMISSION

can	Can I borrow your tennis racquet?
may	May I sit here?
will	Will you please answer the phone?
could	could you please pass the carrots?
would	Would you hand me that pencil?

OTHER AUXILIARY VERBS AND SIMILAR TERMS

used to conveys regularly occurring past activity

Keith used to live in Chicago.
Did Keith used to live in Chicago?

would rather conveys preference

Beth would rather leave earlier than later.
Would Beth rather leave earlier than later?

THE PASSIVE FORM OF VERBS

The passive form of verbs helps express the idea that someone or something is the object of an action. These verbs consist of *be* plus the past participle form of the main verb. Passive structures occur in statements or questions with or without a modal auxiliary. Passive structures might also express a state of existence. These are called stative passive verbs.

Passive Verb Statements
Simple present -- *The child is protected by the dog. The child is protected. (stative passive)*
Present progressive -- *The child is being protected by the dog.*
Present perfect -- *The child has been protected by the dog*
Simple past -- *The child was protected by the dog.*
Past progressive -- *The child was being protected by the dog.*
Past perfect -- *The child had been protected by the dog.*
Simple future -- *The child will be protected by the dog.*
Future perfect -- *The child will have been protected by the dog.*

Passive Verb Questions
Simple present -- *Is the child protected by the dog? Is the child protected? (stative passive)*
Present progressive -- *Is the child being protected by the dog?*
Present perfect -- *Has the child been protected by the dog?*
Simple past -- *Was the child protected by the dog?*
Past progressive -- *Was the child being protected by the dog?*
Past perfect -- *Had the child been protected by the dog?*
Simple future -- *Will the child be protected by the dog?*
Future perfect -- *Will the child have been protected by the dog?*

Passive Verb Statements Including Modals
The child can (cannot, can't) be protected.
The child could (not, couldn't) be protected.
The child had better (not) be protected.
The child is (isn't) supposed to be protected.
The child is (isn't) able (is unable) to be protected.
The child has (hasn't) got to be protected.
The child may (not) be protected.
The child might (not) be protected.
The child must (not, mustn't) be protected.
The child ought to (ought not) be protected.
The child should (not, shouldn't) be protected.
The child (did not, didn't) use to be protected.
The child will (will not, won't) be protected.
The child would (not, wouldn't) be protected. (as per past experience)
The child would rather (not) be protected (than ...).
The child has to (doesn't have to) be protected.

Passive Verb Questions Including Modals
Can (can't) the child be protected?
Could (couldn't) the child be protected?
Had the child not (Hadn't the child better) be protected?
May the child be protected?
Might the child be protected?
Must (mustn't) the child be protected?
Should (shouldn't) the child (Should the child not) be protected?
Didn't the child used to (Did the child not used to) be protected?
Would (wouldn't) the child be protected? (as per past experience)
Wouldn't the child rather (Would the child rather not) be protected (than ...)?
Doesn't the child have to (Does the child not have to) be protected?

REPORTED SPEECH or INDIRECT DISCOURSE

Indirect discourse refers to or reports what someone has said without directly quoting the speaker. Instead, in statements of indirect discourse or reported speech a noun clause is used to report what has been said. If the verb in the statement reporting another's speech (*said*, or a variant) is in the past the verb in the noun clause will generally be a past form as well. The present tense might occur when the reported sentence states a generally accepted fact. When the reporting verb (*said* or variant) is simple present, present perfect or future the noun clause verb tense does not change. Questions of indirect discourse are formed by inverting the subject/verb order of the reporting verb.

Contrasting direct quotes and indirect discourse (reported speech)
He said, "I enjoy ice cream." --- He said that he enjoyed ice cream.
He said, "I am enjoying some ice cream." --- He said (that) he was enjoying some ice cream.
He said, "I have enjoyed ice cream." --- He said he had enjoyed ice cream.
He said, "I enjoyed the ice cream." --- He said he had enjoyed the ice cream.
He said, "I was enjoying the ice cream." --- He said he was enjoying the ice cream.
He said, "I will enjoy the ice cream." ---He said that he will (would) enjoy the ice cream.
He said, "I won't enjoy the ice cream." ---He said that he will not enjoy the ice cream.

Questions expressing indirect discourse (reported speech)
Does he say that he enjoys ice cream?
Did he say (that) he was enjoying the ice cream?
Did he say he had enjoyed the ice cream?
Did he say he enjoyed the ice cream?
Did he say he was enjoying the ice cream?
Did he say he would (will) enjoy the ice cream?
Did he say that he won't (will not) enjoy the ice cream?
Did he say that he should enjoy the ice cream?

CONDITIONAL STATEMENTS

Some statements state facts that are contingent on conditions. These sentences are formed with the verbs of the resulting clauses corresponding to the verbs of the conditional clauses. If the verb of the resulting clause is simple present or simple future, the verb of the conditional (if) clause is simple present. If the verb of the conditional clause is simple past the verb of the resulting clause is the simple form preceded by *would*. If the verb of the conditional clause is past perfect the verb of the resulting class is the past participle preceded by *would have*. In conditional questions, the subject/verb order of the resulting clause is inverted.

Conditional statements
If I have enough money I buy new shirts.
If I have enough money I will buy a new shirt.
If I had enough money I would buy a new shirt.
If I had had enough money I would have bought a new shirt.

Conditional questions
If you have enough money do you buy new shirts?
If you have enough money will you buy a new shirt?
If you had enough money would you buy a new shirt?
If you had had enough money would you have bought a new shirt?

TAG QUESTIONS

Tag questions are questions formed by adding a question phrase at the end of a sentence. Speakers use tag questions to affirm that information is clear or to invite a response indicating a listener's agreement.

When the speaker expects an affirmative answer she uses an affirmative statement and a negative tag.

A speaker, expecting an affirmative answer:

I'm finished, aren't I?
You're finished, aren't you?
He's finished, isn't he?
We're finished, aren't we?
They're finished, aren't they?

When the speaker expects a negative answer he uses a negative statement and an affirmative tag.

A speaker, expecting a negative answer:

I'm not finished, am I?
You're not finished, are you?
She's not finished, is she?
We're not finished, are we?
They're not finished, are they?

QUESTION WORDS

What refers to things

Who refers to a person or persons

Whom refers to a person or persons used as the object of a verb

When refers to time

Where refers to place

How refers to procedure or method

Whose refers to posession

Which refers to selecting one of a known group

How many/how much refers to number or amount

Why refers to reason

Introduction – Section 3

This section contains over 40 pages of materials to help students of elementary grades through adults improve their ability to ask questions.

Each of the first eighteen pages of this section (pp. 73-90) focuses on a particular syntactic or morphemic element. These pages are highly structured, each presenting several items intended to reinforce the target element. Often students are required to interact with a partner asking and answering questions. In many cases questions are written out fully and require a complete sentence answer. Such activities provide students with the opportunity to practice expressing proper question forms and to formulate complex response statements. This repetition enhances students' learning of proper question forms and helps establish their ability to monitor their own question and sentence production.

The exercises on pp. 91-113 do not focus on specific syntactic or morphemic elements, but rather challenge students in a variety of ways. These include unscrambling sentences, matching questions to answers, questioning multiple-meaning statements and composing questions to obtain information.

*These questions ask about things that happen in a regular or ongoing manner. Ask a partner these questions. He or she should answer in full sentences, first, a sentence beginning with **yes**, then a sentence beginning with **no**.*

Example:
Do you like ice cream?
Yes, I like ice cream.
No, I don't like ice cream.

1. Do you want more juice?
2. Do you know how to play chess?
3. Do you ride the bus to school?
4. Do you eat cereal for breakfast?
5. Do you live on a farm?
6. Do you speak another language?
7. Do you drive?
8. Do you use your computer often?
9. Do you have a dog?
10. Do you play baseball?

*These questions ask about things your partner did or did not (didn't) do at some time in the past. Ask these questions. He or she should answer in full sentences, first a sentence beginning with **yes**, then a sentence beginning with **no**.*

Example:
Did you enter the contest?
Yes, I entered the contest.
No, I didn't enter the contest.

1. Did you go to the doctor?
2. Did you listen to the concert on the radio?
3. Did you help the neighbors look for their cat?
4. Did you walk to the party?
5. Did you fix the flat tire?
6. Did you talk to your grandpa yesterday?
7. Did you bake these brownies?
8. Did you rake the leaves?
9. Did you like that movie?
10. Did you wait until after the train stopped to get your bag?

These questions ask about things your partner will or will not (won't) do some time in the future. Ask these questions. He or she should answer in full sentences, first a sentence beginning with **yes**, then a sentence beginning with **no**.

Example:
Will you call me when you get there?
Yes, I will call you when I get there.
No, I won't call you when I get there.

1. Will you return the book tomorrow?
2. Will you buy a birthday gift for Henry?
3. Will you take care of my dog next week?
4. Will you finish your homework by four o'clock?
5. Will you answer the phone?
6. Will you sign up for wrestling this fall?
7. Will you clean out your locker after school?
8. Will you carry these papers out to the garage?
9. Will you eat lunch before you leave?
10. Will you ride your bike to the fair?

*Pretend like you are asking a friend if something is true. your partner should answer with a full sentence beginning with **yes**, then with a full sentence beginning with **no**.*

Example:
Does your dog sleep in the kitchen?
Yes, he sleeps in the kitchen.
No, he doesn't sleep in the kitchen.

1. Does your teacher give homework on Fridays?
2. Does your brother have a bike?
3. Does your mom work at the hospital?
4. Do your teammates like the coach?
5. Do you enjoy cook-outs?
6. Do I look okay?
7. Do they live in your neighborhood?
8. Do we go to the library on Tuesdays?
9. Do chefs go to cooking school?
10. Do doctors study medicine for many years?
11. Does your doctor recommend exercise?
12. Do carpenters use hammers?
13. Does your mom play golf?
14. Does the principal make announcements every day?
15. Does spaghetti sauce have spices in it?
16. Does cheese come from cream?
17. Do elephants eat meat?
18. Do dinosaurs live anywhere on Earth today?
19. Do they live on other planets?
20. Does a cat purr when she's happy?
21. Does a mechanic work at a garage?
22. Do babies sleep a lot?
23. Does winter come before autumn?
24. Do trucks carry dangerous chemicals?
25. Do police officers wear uniforms?
26. Does pollution come from cars?
27. Do tigers live on farms?
28. Does it rain a lot in a jungle?
29. Does it rain a lot in a desert?
30. Do people pay taxes every year?
31. Does corn grow in the winter?
32. Do reindeer have antlers?
33. Do portable radios need batteries?
34. Do fish breathe like people do?
35. Does a computer have a brain?

74

*Pretend that you are asking someone if something did or did not (didn't) happen or if someone did or didn't do something. Your partner should answer in a full sentence beginning with **yes**, then with a full sentence beginning with **no**. Pay close attention to the verb in each question. The verb will be different in the **yes** and the **no** answers.*

Example:
Did you like the movie?
Yes, I liked the movie.
No, I didn't like the movie.

1. Did you work yesterday?
2. Did you play second base in the game last week?
3. Did you finish your book report?
4. Did you help your dad paint the fence?
5. Did you wait for the train at our stop?
6. Did you run in the race last week-end?
7. Did you write a letter to Max?
8. Did you read the story about the flood?
9. Did you understand what she said?
10. Did you hear the new recording of this song?
11. Did you see that program on TV last night?
12. Did you sleep late this morning?
13. Did you wake up early?
14. Did you stay up late last night?
15. Did you eat breakfast with your family?
16. Did you leave the party early?
17. Did you put the puzzles away?
18. Did you call Mr. Schultz about the job?
19. Did you pay for the food already?
20. Did you empty the waste basket?
21. Did he take the trash out?
22. Did she say anything before she left?
23. Did Paul eat lunch with you yesterday?
24. Did we leave early enough to catch the bus?
25. Did we win?
26. Did they hear us?
27. Did she want us to wait for her?
28. Did they think that we were going to be late?
29. Did they know that we were bringing the dog?
30. Did you tell them that I broke the window?
31. Did I leave my backpack at your house yesterday?
32. Did she remember her report?
33. Did she forget to tell you about the time change?
34. Did they find the missing boat off the north coast?
35. Did we get here in time to see the clown?

75

*Ask your partner if something or someone will be doing something at some time in the future. She should answer in a full sentence beginning with **yes**, then in a full sentence beginning with **no**.*

Example:
Will you use your umbrella tomorrow?
Yes, I'll use my umbrella tomorrow.
No, I won't use my umbrella tomorrow.

1. Will you come home early today?
2. Will we need to return these books this week?
3. Are we going to arrive late?
4. Will they shop at the mall?
5. Will you ride the bus to the game?
6. Are you going to talk to Bruce later this afternoon?
7. Is she really going to dance in the show tonight?
8. Will the construction workers finish the house before winter begins?
9. Is he going to get the cast off his leg next week?
10. Will there be enough seats on the plane for our whole team?
11. Are all of your aunts and uncles going to drive to the family reunion?
12. Will the robin build a nest in the big tree behind the house?
13. Are the stores going to stay opened late until Christmas?
14. Will the plumber come to finish the job today?
15. Is the car going to sound different after it's fixed?
16. Will they ask to see my identification?
17. Are they going to give special awards to the people who saved the animals?
18. Will you write a thank-you note to Aunt Martha?
19. Will she graduate next year?
20. Is he going to trim the hedges next to the house?
21. Are the soldiers going to take food to the people across the river?
22. Will he read this chapter before he takes the test?
23. Will your grandmother take her pickle relish to the county fair this year?
24. Is your grandpa going to play the guitar at the festival next week?
25. Are they going to work on the roof before the next rainstorm comes?
26. Will she put snow tires on her car this winter?
27. Is your family going to move to Kansas next summer?
28. Will your cousins come with us on our bike trip to Maine?
29. Is she going to ring the bell so we can come in?
30. Are the swallows going to return to Capistrano next March?

Ask your partner if someone is doing something or something is happening now, happened in the past or will happen in the future. He should answer in a full sentence beginning with **yes**, then in a full sentence beginning with **no**.

> Example:
> Are you working on your project?
> Yes, I'm working on my project.
> No, I'm not working on my project.

1. Are you waiting for the announcement?
2. Is he looking for his bookbag?
3. Are they sitting on the beach?
4. Am I standing on your foot?
5. Is she reading the instructions for the camera?
6. Was she watching the game last night?
7. Were you working on your homework?
8. Were they camping in the woods during the storm?
9. Was I standing where you thought I'd be?
10. Were we looking at the right map?
11. Will you be leaving right after school?
12. Will he be wearing his uniform to practice?
13. Will the principal be coming into our class today?
13. Will they be coming with us?
14. Will I be working behind the counter tonight?
15. Are they having a nice trip?
16. Is he babysitting today?
17. Is the doctor examining George's arm?
18. Were the drivers going too fast?
19. Is she going to be playing in the symphony next season?
20. Are we waiting for the waiter to take our order?
21. Will he be coming to take our order soon?
22. Was she using the computer to analyze the results?
23. Are they going to be broadcasting the Olympics via satellite?
24. Were the police questioning the suspect?
25. Was the scientist reporting the results of her to study to the news reporters last night?
26. Is he taking a make-up test in the library?
27. Are they listening to the president's speech?
28. Will you be joining the group after the program?
29. Are we all working toward the same goal?
30. Will I be receiving a response in the mail?
31. Is she working at the restaurant where her brother works?
32. Are the firefighters going to be marching in the parade?
33. Are you planning your summer vacation yet?
34. Is Bill taking the dog for a walk?
35. Are all of the basketball players practicing in the gym?

Ask your partner if someone is doing something or something is happening now, happened in the past or will happen in the future. Begin your questions with the words **don't**, **isn't**, **aren't**, **wasn't**, **weren't**, or **won't**. Your partner should answer a full sentence beginning with the word, **yes** then a full sentence beginning with the word **no**.

Example:
Aren't you studying for the social studies test?
Yes, I'm studying.
No, I'm not studying.

1. Aren't you planning to come with us?
2. Isn't he mowing his grandparents' lawn?
3. Wasn't she in the chorus in that show?
4. Won't they play the game if it rains?
5. Aren't they sitting at the wrong table?
6. Weren't you waiting for your brother?
7. Didn't she write a letter to the president?
8. Aren't you returning to your job next year?
9. Won't they travel all over Europe?
10. Aren't they going to offer Spanish next semester?
11. Isn't the computer working?
12. Didn't the teachers attend a meeting in the auditorium this morning?
13. Wasn't the contractor explaining this construction project to the mayor?
14. Isn't she working on her master's degree?
15. Weren't they planning to join us for dinner?
16. Aren't they going to finish the project?
17. Doesn't he work in your office?
18. Didn't he use his grandmother's recipe for this sauce?
19. Won't they call us before they announce the decision?
20. Don't you speak Chinese?
21. Didn't the announcer ask for volunteers from the audience?
22. Wasn't the dog chasing the rabbit?
23. Didn't you leave the books on the table in the dining room?
24. Weren't there any messages on the answering machine?
25. Won't they move into the house after it's built?
26. Isn't there any ice in the freezer?
27. Don't we have to wait in line to have our tickets punched?
28. Isn't the officer arresting that drunk driver?
29. Aren't they testing a new kind of electric car?
30. Didn't we arrive on time?
31. Don't the farmers deliver their produce every Tuesday?
32. Isn't the new Supreme Court justice addressing the Congress at this moment?
33. Didn't the secretary address these envelopes?
34. Wasn't the gardner supposed to plant flowers last spring?
35. Doesn't the painter need a ladder to reach the ceiling?

78

*Ask your partner questions about things that have happened before now. She should answer in a full sentence beginning with **yes**, then a full sentence beginning with **no**.*

Example:
Have you read the new book by Jackie Gem?
Yes, I've read that book.
No, I haven't read that book.

1. Have you met the new neighbors?
2. Have you ever been to Canada?
3. Have you eaten lunch yet?
4. Have you ever eaten at that new French restaurant in town?
5. Have they checked in yet?
6. Have they always lived there?
7. Has he decided to run for mayor?
8. Have they ever met your grandmother?
9. Has it been this cold all winter?
10. Has she started her project yet?
11. Has the painter finished painting the dining room?
12. Have all the children seen the sculpture?
13. Have some of the children been here before?
14. Has everyone met Greg?
15. Has the fifth grade class learned the song?
16. Have all of these students brought in money for the field trip?
17. Has anyone seen Mr. Cameron?
18. Has Debra gotten a chance to use the phone?
19. Have the crops always been so plentiful?
20. Has Pedro found his schedule?
21. Have you forgotten about the meeting?
22. Have Carmella and Lynn received their invitations?
23. Haven't they arrived yet?
24. Hasn't Kevin turned his paper in yet?
25. Haven't you already seen this movie?
26. Haven't we subscribed to that magazine before?
27. Hasn't Rachael found her glasses?
28. Haven't I had any calls?
29. Hasn't the all-clear signal sounded yet?
30. Haven't the Red Sox ever won the World Series?

*Ask your partner about things that happened and were completed before another time in the past or before another activity began. He should answer in a full sentence beginning with **yes**, then a full sentence beginning with **no**.*

Example:
Had you eaten dinner before you got on the train?
Yes, I had.
No, I hadn't.

1. Hadn't they read the instructions before they put the table together?
2. Had Cindy left before you arrived?
3. Had the doctor recommended that medicine before she knew about your allergies?
4. Had the police arrived before the explosion?
5. Had they taken any pictures before the camera broke?
6. Hadn't the principal talked to the teachers before the assembly?
7. Had they noticed that the roof leaked before the big storm?
8. Hadn't the electrician turned off the power before he left?
9. Hadn't the workers finished the job before the furniture arrived?
10. Hadn't they announced the results before they were printed in the newspaper?
11. Had the traffic pattern changed before the highway construction began?
12. Had we heard of the possibility of this change before it happened?
13. Had she tried out for a part in this play the last time it was performed?
14. Had they received the invitations early enough to make plans before the party?
15. Hadn't the manager warned the staff about the delays before they went to the airport?
16. Had she found your wallet before you realized that it was missing?
17. Had we driven down this road before this traffic light was here?
18. Had he learned to play the trumpet before he learned to play the trombone?
19. Had you mailed the letter before she called?
20. Hadn't the tailor taken measurements before he began to make the suit?

Pretend that you want to know how long your friend or others have been doing something. Ask questions to find out.

You want to know how long some people have lived in the places where they are now living.

> **Example:**
> You want to know how long Heather has lived in Dallas.
> Ask, "How long has Heather been living in Dallas?"

1. Keith ... New Mexico
2. Rinaldo ... Chicago
3. Carolyn ... Paris
4. Shannon ... Saudi Arabia
5. Mark ... New York City
6. Diane and her sister ... New Orleans
7. Keesha and her family ... Kansas City
8. Benito ... Los Angeles
9. Kathy and her family ... Miami
10. Jonathon ... Huntsville, Alabama

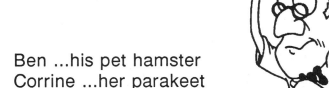

You want to know how long each of these people has had something.

> **Example:**
> You want to know how long Jill has had her car.
> Ask, "How long has Jill had her car?"

1. Ben ...his pet hamster
2. Corrine ...her parakeet
3. Adrienne ...her part-time job
4. Dominic ...his motorcycle
5. Fillipe ...his roller blades
6. Lee ...his answering machine
7. Jessica and Kathy ...their paper route
8. Rebecca and Jan ...their uniforms
9. The Swansons ...their convertible
10. Bill, Carlos and Jerry ...their ice cream stand

Each of these people had been looking for something before they found it.

You want to know how long each one had been looking.

> **Example:**
> You want to know how long Seth had been looking for his guitar before he found it.
> Ask, "How long had Seth been looking for his guitar before he found it?"

1. Debra ...her wedding dress
2. Sylvia ...her job
3. Mike ...his keys
4. Roseanne ...her sweater
5. Mrs. Malone ...this antique tea kettle
6. Mr. Jones ...just the right birthday gift for his daughter
7. Ben Franklin ...electricity
8. You ...my house
9. Your dog ...his bone
10. Aunt Sophie ...this recipe for fudge cake

81

*Ask your partner each of these questions. She should answer each question with a full sentence beginning with **yes**, then with a full sentence beginning with **no**.*

> Example:
> Should Dan wait for us?
> Yes, Dan should wait for us.
> No, he shouldn't wait for us.

1. Should we hand in our papers before we leave?
2. Can she drive the tractor?
3. May I borrow your umbrella?
4. Do we have to sign out before we leave?
5. Shouldn't we take our books back today?
6. Could you talk to your neighbor about using his driveway?
7. Are you able to take both dogs for a walk at the same time?
8. Can't you walk faster than that?
9. Hadn't we better get there a little early?
10. Didn't he used to drive a convertible?

You want to know about some things. Ask questions to find out what you want to know.

You want to know if...
...fish can fly.
...dogs can bark
...George can use a computer
...horses can run faster than tigers
...colored photographs can be faxed

You want to know if I (self)...
...may borrow your pen
...may copy your notes
...may have more peaches
...may take your plate
...may be excused

You want to know if...
...Paul should be awake by now
...Derek should call his dad
...we should bake two or three dozen brownies
...you should lock the door before you leave
...the dog should get a rabies shot this year

You want to know if...
...the Smiths used to own this house
...dinosaurs used to live around here
...Mike used to deliver newspapers
...this lake used to be clean enough for swimming
...Meredeth used to work for the Los Angeles Times

You want to know if...
...you have got to be in school tomorrow
...we have got to write poems for English class
...Sue has got to stay at work late tonight
...Ben has got to have a physical before he goes to camp
...they have got to wait in line

You are trying to find out about these possibilities; you want to know if you (another person) could...
...drive anyone to the airport
...leave this article for me to read when you're finished
...put the food away after dinner is over
...help put the children to bed
...try to reschedule some of these appointments

*Pretend that you are talking to your teacher or a classmate asking what is **supposed to** happen or what someone is **supposed to** do. Your partner should answer in a full sentence beginning with **yes**, then a sentence beginning with **no**, pretending to be your teacher or classmate.*

Example:
Am I supposed to sit here?
Yes, you are supposed to sit here.
No, you're not supposed to sit here. or..
No, you aren't supposed to sit here.

1. Am I supposed to write in cursive?
2. Am I supposed to put my lunch in my locker?
3. Am I supposed to finish page 29 for homework?
4. Am I supposed to take this book to the library?
5. Am I supposed to give this note to the principal?
6. Am I supposed to buy a lunch ticket?
7. Was I supposed to bring in money for the field trip?
8. Was I supposed to close the window?
9. Are we supposed to answer these questions?
10. Are we supposed to correct our test papers?
11. Are you supposed to sit in front of me?
12. Are you supposed to trade books with me?
13. Are you supposed to help me with my math?
14. Are we supposed to work together on our science projects?
15. Are we supposed to get our pictures taken today?
16. Are we supposed to see a movie this afternoon?
17. Were we supposed to buy our tickets from the coach?
18. Are we supposed to go to gym at one o'clock?
19. Were we supposed to wait for the announcement?
20. Are we supposed to bring our own pencils?
21. Is there supposed to be a storm?
22. Is there supposed to be a fire drill this morning?
23. Is he supposed to share those markers with us?
24. Is she supposed to be on our team?
25. Was he supposed to know about the party?
26. Is she supposed to call us?
27. Are they supposed to be ready yet?
28. Are they supposed to announce the winner soon?
29. Were they supposed to deliver the pizza for our party?
30. Were they supposed to come with us?

*Ask your partner about these possibilities. He should answer each in a full sentence beginning with **yes**, then a full sentence beginning with **no**.*

Example:
Can these packages be sent out today?
Yes, they can be sent out today.
No, they can't be sent out today.

1. Should the furniture be removed from the living room before the painters arrive?
2. Can't this door be unlocked from the inside?
3. Shouldn't this window be closed?
4. Can this casserole be frozen?
5. Can these shoes be worn at the beach?
6. Are these books supposed to covered?
7. Should these videos be returned today?
8. Can we watch one of the videos before you return them?
9. Can't the volume on the TV be turned down?
10. Weren't we supposed to be introduced?
11. Shouldn't she have been taught how to use this computer?
12. Hadn't this smoke detector better be checked right away?
13. Should all of these problems be written out?
14. Shouldn't this check have been deposited in your account?
15. Haven't the errors been corrected yet?
16. Won't the paper be delivered today?
17. Are these seeds supposed to be planted in your garden?
18. Should this plant be watered twice a week?
19. Will the stove be repaired in time to fix dinner?
20. Is the water supposed to be turned back on this afternoon?
21. Doesn't he have to be told about the meeting?
22. Will the picnic be cancelled if it rains?
23. Can I be guaranteed that this machine will work for one year?
24. Shouldn't this job be finished by now?
25. Were we supposed to be warned about the storm?
26. Wouldn't we have been picked up sooner if we had called?
27. Will we be prepared to do the job if we take this course?
28. Wouldn't he have been protected if he had worn a seat belt?
29. Shouldn't the trucks carrying dangerous chemicals be forced to travel on roads that don't go through town?
30. Shouldn't laws be written to protect the people from injustice?

Example:
    You want to know if the door was locked.
    Was the door locked?

You want to know if these people were invited to these events:

...Charlie ...your cousin's wedding
...Rinaldo ...the dance
...Mrs. McCarthy ...the luncheon
...Mr. and Mrs. Gardner ...your parents dinner party
...the next-door neighbors ...our barbecue

You want to know if the following materials or supplies were ordered from each of these businesses:

...books ...the publisher
...pills ...the pharmacist
...flowers ...the florist
...rolls ...the bakery
...pictures ...the photographer
...ball point pens ...the office supply store

You want to know if each of these things was sent to the right person:

...wedding invitation ...Chariie
...bank statement ...my accountant
...test results ...the students
...books ...the science teacher
...bandages ...the veterinarian

You want to know if these things will be finished tomorrow:

...the project
...the dry cleaning
...the experiment
...the judging
...the painting

Ask questions about what someone has said.

For each item:
a) read the quotation,
b) read the statement about the quotation,
c) ask a question about the quotation.

1. a) Bill said, "I am working on my report."
   b) Bill said that he was working on his report.
   c) ....?
2. a) "I've been working on my report for six hours," said Bill.
   b) Bill said that he has been working on his report for six hours.
   c) ....?
3. a) Bill said, "I had been writing my report for six hours when my wrist started to hurt."
   b) Bill said that he'd been writing his report for six hours when his wrist started to hurt.
   c) ....?
4. a) "You should get more exercise," the doctor told Amy.
   b) The doctor told Amy that she should get more exercise.
   c) ....?
5. a) "Do you want my juice?" asked Bev.
   b) Bev asked if I wanted her juice.
   c) ....?

Here, only the quotation is provided. Read each quotation. Say a statement reporting what each person said (as in "b", above). Then ask a question about what each person said (as in "c", above).

1. a) "I like pizza with pepperoni," said Gail.
   b) ....   c) ....?
2. a) Jeff said, "I want another sandwich."
   b) ....   c) ....?
3. a) "I can drive to the game," said Kathleen.
   b) ....   c) ....?
4. a) "You are a good writer," the teacher told Carlos.
   b) ....   c) ....?
5. a) Maria said, "I've been waiting for the bus for an hour."
   b) ....   c) ....?

6. a) "I had been waiting for the bus for an hour when it started to rain," said Maria.
   b) ....   c) ....?
7. a) "I'm going to try out for the basketball team," Henry said.
   b) ....   c) ....?
8. a) Florence said, "I found my wallet under the seat."
   b) ....   c) ....?
9. a) "Do you have enough money?" mother asked Phil.
   b) ....   c) ....?
10. a) "Would you like more iced tea?" the waiter asked Molly.
   b) ....   c) ....?

Ask questions to find our information that you need or would like to know. Begin each of your questions with the proper question word.

Ask questions about time. Use the word **when**. You want to know **when**...

> Example:
> ...the game begins
>   When does the game begin?

... Sandy will arrive
... dinner should be ready
... World War II ended
... football season is over

Ask questions about places. Use the word **where**. You want to know **where**...

... your shoes are
... the nearest bus stop is
... you should put the package
... you can find anchovies
... Sue got her necklace

Ask questions about reasons. Use the word **why**. You want to know **why**...

... bears sleep all winter
... cars can't fly
... ice melts
... the days are longer in summer
   than they are in winter

Ask questions about manner or process. Use the word **how**. You want to know **how**...

... airplanes fly
... you fly a kite
... someone can get a chocolate
   stain out of a white shirt
... Seth learned to speak Chinese
... Milt became such a good cook

Ask questions about people. Use the word **who**. You want to know **who**...

... opened the orange juice
... left the cap off the toothpaste tube
... has the pop corn
... went to the meeting last night
... will play second base in the
   game Saturday

Ask questions about possession. Use the word **whose**. You want to know **whose**...

... clothes are in the washer
... turn it is
... dog is barking
... boots are in the hall
... suitcase is still in the van

Ask question about things. Use the word **what**. You want to know **what**...

... Carol has in her purse
... spices Harvey put in this sauce
... you should put on the top shelf
... you need to start planting
   your garden
... Bob got for his birthday

Ask questions about choices. Use the word **which**. You want know **which**...

... book you should bring to class
... restaurant everyone wants
   to go to
... student arrived first
... plan you should use
... car Mark should drive

*Think about finding out what someone will do or how something or someone would be under various conditions. Ask questions using the word **if** to find out what you want to know. Ask your partner these questions to find out what she would do or how something would be under different conditions. She should answer in a full sentence.*

Example:
   Will they cancel the picnic if it rains?
   If it rains, they will cancel the picnic.

1. If we run out of flour can we still bake the bread?
2. Should we go down the basement if we hear storm warning sirens?
3. Will you be disappointed if your sister finds out about the party?
4. Will we be able to have a horse if we have a big back yard?
5. Can we plan to have the meeting at your house if it's just a small group?
6. Will we be in first place if we win the game today?
7. Can I borrow your bike if I promise to be careful?
8. If I find your book should I send it back to you?
9. Do you think you'll pass the test if you study?
10. Do you want to go to the beach if it's warm tomorrow?
11. What will you do if you miss your train?
12. Wouldn't the trip have been easier if we hadn't brought the dog?
13. What should I do if I can't find the key?
14. Will we have enough money for the gift if I put in ten dollars?

You want to know if certain events will take place under each of these condutions. Ask questions to find out.

Example:
   a bad storm...
   a) school will be closed,
      Will school be closed if there's a bad storm?
   b) the roads will be closed
      If there's a bad storm will the roads be closed?

1. a surprise party for mom...
   a) we can get the house cleaned
   b) Sally can keep it a secret

2. Bob has to work Saturday...
   a) mom can drive him to work
   b) he should iron his uniform

3. it snows tomorrow...
   a) we can make a snowman
   b) I should wear my boots

4. I lose my wallet...
   a) I should call the police
   b) I should cancel my credit cards

5. Peggy babysits Saturday night...
   a) she should take some story books
   b) she can get a ride home

6. there's an election...
   a) most people will vote
   b) we will have a new governor

7. our TV is broken...
   a) we should call a repair person
   b) we can rent a TV

8. I get a new car...
   a) I have to get new license plates
   b) I have to buy car insurance

9. our dog gets sick...
   a) we should call the vet
   b) we should give him some medicine

One way to make sure that you understand something clearly, or to make sure that someone else agrees with you is to say a statement with a question added at the end. The statement part says what you think is correct; the question part asks if you are correct.

> Example: Tomorrow is Tuesday, isn't it?
> Your listener will answer, "Yes," or "No."

When you think something is correct you will say the statement and add a question including **not**. *When you think something is not correct* you will say a statement including not and add a question that doesn't include not.

Here you believe something is correct and you are checking to make sure, or trying to find out if your listener agrees:

> "Monday comes before Tuesday, doesn't it?"

Here you think that something is incorrect and you are checking to make sure, or trying to find out if your listener agrees:

> "Tuesday doesn't come before Monday, does it?"

Read the questions below. Think of how the speaker feels about the information. Write **correct** *if you think the speaker believes his information is correct. Write* **incorrect** *if you think the speaker believes his information is not correct.*

1. _____ Apples grow on trees, don't they?
2. _____ Oranges don't grow in Alaska, do they?
3. _____ The mail should be here by now, shouldn't it?
4. _____ The ice cream was delicious, wasn't it?
5. _____ Marco Polo traveled to China, didn't he?
6. _____ Nobody lives on the moon, do they?
7. _____ Police officers aren't required to have black belts in Karate, are they?
8. _____ Oranges contain vitamin C, don't they?
9. _____ You shouldn't ride a bike without a helmet, should you?
10. _____ Larry Bird played for the Boston Celtics, didn't he?

Ask questions like the ones above to make sure that you have correct information, or to find out whether your listener agrees with you.

> Example:
> You think that peanut butter is made from peanuts.
> Peanut butter is made from peanuts, isn't it?
> You didn't think the test was too hard.
> The test wasn't too hard, was it?

1. You think yogurt is nutritious.
2. You think it's expensive to own a car.
3. You think school begins in September.
4. You don't think mail is delivered on Sunday.
5. You don't think it's too cold to go to the beach.
6. You think fruit and vegetables are good for you.
7. You think you should water your garden every day.
8. You don't think you look good in blue.
9. You think snow tires will help you drive better in the winter.
10. You think the bus will come at six o'clock like it's supposed to.

Think about these groups of items. Three out of four items in each group go together because they belong in the same category. Ask a partner **which ones** go together and ask **why**. She should answer by naming the items that are in the same category, and stating that as the reason. Then ask which one **doesn't** belong and **why**. Your partner should answer by naming the item that does not belong to this category and stating that as the reason.

Example:
   apple, orange, shoe, grape...
a. **Which ones go together?**
   The apple, the orange and the grape go together.
b. **Why do they go together?**
   Because they are all fruits.
c. **Which one doesn't belong?**
   The shoe doesn't belong.
d. **Why doesn't it belong?**
   Because the shoe is not a fruit.

1. shirt, sweater, juice, shorts
2. milk, water, tea, hot dog
3. knife, spoon, scissors, saw
4. umbrella, truck, train, airplane
5. candy, syrup, icing, vinegar
6. ice cream, steak, pork chops, hamburger
7. engine, steering wheel, pencil, brakes
8. computer, broom, mop, vacuum cleaner
9. pencil, crayon, comb, pen
10. blocks, kite, ball, apple
11. boots, shoes, hat, slippers
12. salmon, shark, tuna, robin
13. alligator, monkey, dog, cat
14. pillow, rock, fur, feathers
15. lamp, lunch box, toaster, hair dryer
16. tire, pen, notebook, markers
17. carrots, celery, chicken, lettuce
18. one, seventy-four, three hundred and twelve, soup
19. sheet, bottle, jar, jug
20. sofa, table, suitcase, chair
21. ballet, football, basketball, baseball
22. hammer, saw, glass, screw driver
23. George, Fred, James, Darleen
24. driveway, house, tent, apartment
25. street, road, highway, lawn
26. dentist, carpenter, plumber, electrician
27. bandage, crutches, socks, cast
28. farmer, dancer, singer, musician
29. ambulance, sports car, police car, fire engine
30. robin, blue jay, whale, parrot

Unscramble each of these scrambled sentences and form a question. For some there might be more than one way to do this.

1. like lemon tea do your you with
2. dog you have black and do a white
3. police missing the find car the did
4. to supposed tomorrow rain it is
5. like milk your does kitten to drink
6. where key the put you did
7. here Jill when to is get going
8. note give to him to have why we this do
9. the who won contest
10. they that ship bottle the how in did get
11. room table whose in is on the the hat dining
12. game start to time the supposed what is
13. concert drive home us who going the from is to
14. Millie us with why can't come
15. to to fair your is the you take going uncle
16. wait did have you to long how
17. I put should flowers where these
18. Cleveland is from Cincinnati far how
19. dog Paul by chased that was
20. appointment you want do me to you remind about your
21. is the in driveway car whose parked
22. lunch to comming who be will with us
23. you change how tire do a
24. should I your calls what say mother if
25. cake put when you the did in the oven
26. why you for didn't test study the
27. rather which vanilla would chocolate or you have
28. room color you to going what are paint your
29. pepperoni does taste like what
30. butter better like which or margerine you do

91

Each of these statements could be the answer to two or more questions. Read each statement and ask the questions that it might answer. Suggestions telling you the first word of questions are given with each statement.

1. Jenny found her purse on the playground. *What Where Who*

> Example:
> *What* did Jenny find?
> *Where* did Jenny find the purse?
> *Who* found a purse on the playground?

2. Joe's recital will be held on Tuesday evening at 7:30. *What Whose When*

3. Beth didn't go on the hike because she was sick. *Who Why What*

4. Seth likes oil and vinegar dressing on his salad. *Who What kind*

5. Meredeth played left field last season, but her throwing was so accurate that she is a pitcher this season. *Who When Why What position*

6. Mr. Jones converted his swimming pool to a vegetable garden by filling it with dirt and planting seeds. *Who What How*

7. Calvin grows vegetables in his back yard because he likes to eat food that is as fresh as possible. *Who What Why Where*

8. Cook the sauce on low heat and stir it often so it doesn't burn. *What How Why*

9. Bill couldn't buy the new helmet because it cost twenty dollars and he had only ten dollars. *Who What Why How much*

10. Muriel's favorite place to go on vacation is Cape Cod because it's so peaceful and beautiful. *Whose Where Why*

11. Carlos always wears thick, cotton socks when he runs so he doesn't get blisters on his feet. *Who What When Why*

12. Last night we walked to the beach at night so we could see the moon's reflection on the water. *When Where Why What*

13. If it rains cover the tools so they don't get wet. *What Why*

14. The people were warned by the police not to touch the live electric wires on the ground. *Who What Where*

Each of these statements could be the answer to two or more questions. Read each statement and ask the questions that it might answer. Suggestions telling you the first word of questions are given with each statement.

1. No one should touch live electric wires because the electrical charge carried by such wires could kill someone by passing through his body. ***Who What Why How***

Example:
   Who should touch electric wires?
   What if someone touches electric wires?
   Why shouldn't you touch electric wires?
   How can electric wires kill someone?

2. Before electricity was discovered people used to use candles or oil-burning lanterns for light. ***When Who What Why***

3. The McKinneys plan to find a swimming instructor to teach their young daughter to swim. ***Who Why***

4. Anyone who goes into water should know how to swim because if she can't keep herself above water she might die of drowning by inhaling water instead of air into her lungs. ***Who Why How What if***

5. A person will stay above water as long as he can keep his lungs filled with air because this makes his body lighter than water. ***Who Where Why How***

6. A submarine will float if its ballast tanks are filled with air and will move below the water if it's ballast tanks are filled with water. ***What Where What if***

7. A ship is able to move through the water because its engines drive a propeller which moves the water and pushes the ship forward. ***What How Where***

8. A sail boat captain moves her boat through the water by using the power of the wind to push the sail and the boat in a forward direction. ***Who What How Where***

9. Each passenger must have a life jacket so he can stay above water if the boat capsizes and he is thrown off. ***Who What Why What if Where***

10. Ships carry passengers and cargo all over the world. ***What Who Where***

11. Before there were stores and merchants in the colonies of America almost all of the goods used by the colonists were brought in by ship. ***When Where Who How Why***

93

Each of these statements could be the answer to two or more questions. Read each statement and ask the questions that it might answer. Suggestions telling you the first word of questions are given with each statement.

1. Today manufacturers send goods from their own country to other countries so the goods can be sold to people in many countries. **When Who What To whom**

> Example:
> **When** do manufacturers send goods?
> **Who** sends the goods?
> **What** do manufacturers send?
> **To whom** do the goods go?

2. French wine makers are known all over the world for making delicious wine. **Who Where Why What**

3. Swiss craftspeople are famous for making beautiful clocks and watches which are sold all over the world. **Who What Where Why**

4. American musicians are famous all over the world for expressing feelings through creative and exciting music. **Who Where Why How**

5. All countries have special products made by their people that are important to people throughout the world. **Who What How Where**

6. At the last county fair Beth's mother won a blue ribbon for her fruit preserves. **Where When Why Who What**

7. Whenever the sky gets dark, Casey is afraid that there might be a storm. **When Who What**

8. Two years ago the snow outside our back door was so high that we couldn't open our door. **When What Why Who Where**

9. Ken's uncle's plane could not take off because there was a storm. **Who What Why**

10. The principal would not let the children go out for recess yesterday because the playground was covered with ice and he was afraid someone might slip and get hurt. **Who What Why How**

11. Cars are not allowed to park on our street on Tuesdays because the city workers clean our streets. **What When Why Who**

94

Each of these statements could be the answer to two or more questions. Read each statement and ask the questions that it might answer. Suggestions telling you the first word of questions are given with each statement.

1. Jack doesn't like country music so I have to remember to turn the stereo off whenever he comes to our house. *Who What Why When*

   Example:
   Who doesn't like country music?
   What do you do when Jack comes to the house?
   Why do you turn off the stereo?
   When do you turn off the stereo?

2. Michelle couldn't find a carburetor for her old car here in town so she had to order one from a catalogue. *Why What Where*

3. The last time Daniel saw his dentist she warned him that he would have serious problems with his teeth and gums if he does not use dental floss more often. *Why Who When What if What*

4. One day last July the temperature in our city was higher than it has ever been since records have been kept. *When Where What*

5. When it gets really hot outside people should slow down and drink extra liquids so they don't get sick. *When Why What Why*

6. The new car Sara wanted to buy this year cost a thousand dollars more than she had saved so she'll keep driving her old car until she can save more money. *Who What How much When Why*

7. Ray enjoyed driving his new car to Oregon last summer because it was safe and comfortable and it went over forty miles on a gallon of gas. *Who When What Where Why*

8. When Ray got Oregon he had saved so much money on gas that he was able to take his cousins out to dinner four times. *Who Where How much Why How many*

9. My mom really likes the family to have dinner at a restaurant so she doesn't have to cook. *Why What Where Why*

10. Nancy lost her first tooth at her fifth birthday party. *Why Where What When*

95

Think about tools, materials or instruments that various specialists need in order to do their jobs. Of course, if one of them did not have a particular tool or material he or she could not do something important to his or her work.

In this exercise you will ask questions to find out **why** a certain worker needs a certain tool or material (reason), and **what would happen if** this worker did not have this item (result). Your partner should answer each question in a full sentence.

Example:
artist... brush... paint a picture
Why does an artist need a brush? (reason)
An artist needs a brush so he can paint a picture.
What if an artist didn't have a brush? (result)
If an artist didn't have a brush he couldn't paint pictures.

1. baker... oven... bake bread and cakes
2. scientist... microscope... look at tiny specimens
3. photographer... camera... take photos
4. scuba diver... oxygen tank... breathe under water
5. pilot... radio... talk to the control tower
6. ballerina... stage... perform before an audience
7. football player... shoulder pads... protect himself from injuries
8. jockey... horse... ride in a race
9. judge... gavel... bring court to order
10. broadcaster... microphone... speak to the broadcast audience
11. lumberjack... chain saw... cut down trees
12. librarian... bookshelves... keep books in order
13. lifeguard... high chair... see all sections of the pool
14. barber... scissors... trim hair
15. sailor... compass... find the right direction
16. gas station attendant... gas... fill customers' gas tanks
17. astronomer... telescope... study stars and planets
18. chemist... test tube... study how chemicals react with each other
19. electrician... wire... make electrical connections
20. doctor... stethoscope... listen to heartbeat
21. plumber... soldering torch... solder pipe fittings
22. gardener... greenhouse... control moisture and temperature for growing plants
23. hair stylist... conditioner... make hair manageable
24. miner... head lamp... see in a dark mine
25. jeweler... gold... make gold jewelry

Think about tools, materials or instruments that various specialists need in order to do their jobs. Of course, if one of them did not have a particular tool or material he or she could not do something important to his or her work.
In this exercise you will ask questions to find out **why** *a certain worker needs a certain tool or material (reason), and* **what would happen if** *this worker did not have this item (result). Your partner should answer each question in a full sentence.*

Example:
artist... brush... paint a picture
Why does an artist need a brush? (reason)
An artist needs a brush so he can paint a picture.
What if an artist didn't have a brush? (result)
If an artist didn't have a brush he couldn't paint pictures.

1. nurse... thermometer... take patients' temperatures
2. police officer... police car... move through traffic quickly and safely
3. waiter... order pad... write down customers' orders
4. author... copyright... protect her work from being copied
5. tailor... tape measure... take people's measurements
6. potter... kiln... fire pottery
7. weaver... loom... weave fibers into cloth
8. carpenter... drill... drill holes
9. sculptor... chisel... shape stone
10. farmer... silo... store grain
11. cook... spices... add flavors to foods
12. astronaut... space ship... travel in space
13. brick layer... trowel... put mortar on bricks
14. custodian... mop... clean floors
15. crossing guard... sign... caution cars to stop
16. fisherman... bait... lure fish
17. trucker... truck... haul loads of goods long distances
18. painter... brush... apply paint to surfaces
19. teacher... chalk... write on a chalkboard
20. writer... words... communicate ideas to other people
21. gardener... seeds... plant crops
22. rancher... grazing land... let cows graze
23. chef... refrigerator... keep food cold
24. postman... mail sack... carry a large amount of mail as he walks
25. dentist... drill... remove decayed part of a tooth

Each item is a group of 3 or 4 words. For each item ask a question containing all of the words.

CHALLENGE YOURSELF...
Try asking questions using at least 6 words, 8 words, or 12 words!

1. Sue play go
2. where dinner Tuesday
3. happen storm tonight
4. how money have
5. what Sue lunch
6. who invited party
7. when book library
8. much cost sweater
9. Wayne letter write
10. Kevin book about
11. will return time
12. should turn left
13. Ronda pizza order
14. can more please
15. tomorrow cloudy will
16. anyone shoes my
17. again back should
18. doesn't anymore here
19. you throw away
20. how get airport
21. ever before Canada
22. want beach you
23. won't her later
24. shouldn't longer wait
25. appointment dentist's when
26. program how VCR
27. drive car whose
28. helmet bike have
29. better today feeling
30. arrived accident we

31. dog take walk
32. street bumpy is
33. new car did
34. what Eddie matter
35. freezer should put
36. want you which
37. hers blue umbrella
38. correct address your
39. number phone do
40. can until week
41. stay until over
42. sad was ceremony
43. you believe happened
44. them for should
45. better wouldn't if
46. call emergency you
47. long drive you
48. this distance phone call
49. finish report fish
50. president say about
51. celebrate how birthday
52. surprise party was
53. have ticket train
54. more need time
55. CPR did save
56. dangerous climb cliff
57. shouldn't call taxi
58. enough everyone has
59. video ceremony see
60. angry he broken

*Here is a list of important days or traditions that are celebrated in the United States. Also given is the month(s) when each is celebrated and a brief statement of the purpose of each holiday. Using this information practice asking questions to find out **when** and **why** each is celebrated. Also using the information, your partner should answer your questions.*

Example:
  When do we celebrate New Year's Day?
  January.
  Why do we celebrate New Year's Day?
  Because it's the first day of the new year.

1.	Martin Luther King Day	January	Commemorates the teachings of Martin Luther King, a famous civil rights leader
2.	Valentine's Day	February	Feast of St. Valentine, the patron saint of lovers
3.	Presidents' Day	February	Commemorates presidents of the United States
4.	St. Patrick's Day	March	Feast of the patron Saint of Ireland
5.	Passover	March or April	Commemorates the time when Moses led the Jews out of Egypt
6.	Easter	March or April	Celebrates the day when Jesus Christ rose from the dead
7.	Mothers' Day	May	Honors all mothers
8.	Memorial Day	May	Commemorates the dead servicemen and women of all wars in which the United States participated
9.	Flag Day	June	Anniversary of the day in 1777 when the American flag was adopted
10.	Fathers' Day	June	Honors all fathers
11.	Independence Day	July	Celebrates American independence from British rule
12.	Labor Day	September	Honors all laborers in the United States and Canada
13.	Holloween	October	The eve of the feast of All Saints, generally celebrated with masquerading and fun
14.	Thanksgiving	November	A day for giving thanks; commemorates the Pilgrims' celebration of the good harvest of 1621
15.	Chanukah	December	Commemorates the rededication of Jews to their religious ancestry; the rededication of the temple in Jeruselem and return to traditional worship of the Jews
16.	Christmas	December	Celebrates the birth of Jesus Christ
17.	Kwanzaa	December	African Americans reflect on the seven principles of black culture: unity, self-determination, collective work and responsibility, cooperative economics, purpose, creativity, and faith; Inspired by African harvest festivals

Practice asking questions about what someone has said. Read the conversations on the left and pretend that someone other than yourself heard the conversations. You are interested, and want to know what the speakers said. Ask a question for each of the items on the right.

1. "I heard the weather forecast on my way home from work," said Mrs. Kennedy. "Looks like we're going to have a blizzard tonight. We could have 12 inches of snow by morning."

1. You want to know if Mrs. Kennedy said:
   a. that she heard the weather report
   b. that there might be a blizzard tonight
   c. if she knew how much snow there might be.

2. "Is that so!" said Mr. Kennedy. "It sure hasn't looked like snow all day. In fact, the sky's been clear and the sun's been out most of the day. Gina just got home from school and Max is upstairs working on his science report. I'll tell them about the snow."

2. You want to know if Mr. Kennedy said:
   a. that Gina was home from school
   b. that Max was doing his math homework
   c. that the sky looked dark and cloudy all day.

3. "Gina! Max! Mom just heard that there's going to be a blizzard tonight. We might have 12 inches of snow by morning. We'll have to listen for school closing announcements."

3. You want to know if Mr Kennedy told Gina and Max:
   a. that mom said that there might be 12 inches of snow by morning
   b. that they should listen for school closing information.

4. "That's great!" said Max. "If there's no school tomorrow I'll be able to spend more time on this science project. I'm having trouble trying to explain some of these experiments."

4. You want to know if Max said:
   a. that he could work on his science project if there was no school tomorrow
   b. that he was having some trouble with his science project.

5. "I'll help you with your science project tonight," Gina said to Max. If there's a lot of snow tomorrow we shouldn't waste the day inside. We should go sledding or cross-country skiing. Winter's almost over. We might not have another chance to use our sleds and skis."

5. You want to know if Gina said:
   a. that she could help Max with his science project
   b. what she'd like to do tomorrow if there's a lot of snow
   c. that winter was just beginning

100

In this exercise you will ask questions to get information about events. When you hear or read about an event, you must get enough information to enable you to participate, or tell someone about the event, or to know all that has happened during a past event. Read each paragraph. You will notice that each sentence in the paragraph is numbered. Each sentence is supposed to give a bit of information about the event. Following each paragraph is a list of numbers corresponding with the numbers of the sentences in the paragraph. For each of these items ask a question or questions which the sentence answers. The first word of each question is given.

(1)The Centerville Soccer Team will hold a bake sale next week. (2)The soccer players need new uniforms and they decided to see if they could raise the money by having a bake sale. (3)The bake sale will be held after practice next Tuesday evening, about 6:00P.M. (4)It will be set up in the parking lot near the front gate. (5)The families of the players are being asked to contribute cakes, cookies, bread or other treats, and the soccer players and their parents will sell the baked goods. (6)The soccer players will make signs and put them up in neighborhood stores so that people will find out about the bake sale. (7)The soccer players hope they can raise $75.00 at this bake sale.

1. What
   Who
2. Why
3. When
4. Where
5. Who
   What
6. How
   Where
   What
7. How much

---

(1)Our science teacher would like to have a zoologist speak to our class. (2)We are studying reptiles and amphibians and he can't answer some of our questions, so he invited Marty Cannon form the Millville Zoo. (3)Marty is the director of the Millville Zoo, and also teaches zoology at the junior college in Millville. (4)She has traveled to many countries and has studied at different universities in order to learn as much as possible about reptiles and amphibians. (5)She will speak to our class next Thursday afternoon. (6)Science class will be held out on the grass in front of the school next Thursday so the animals that Marty brings will be more comfortable. (7)Our teacher said that we can invite our parents, brothers and sisters to science class next Thursday so they can learn more about reptiles and amphibians too.

1. Who
2. Why
   Who
3. Who
4. How
   Where
5. When
6. Where
   Why
7. Who
   When

---

(1)Each fall the police officers and firefighters in our town put on a musical play. (2)They sell tickets and raise money for the homeless people in our town. (3)Also, many of the officers and firefighters really enjoy performing on stage! (4)The police desk sargent has a great voice and usually plays a leading roll. (5)Two of the firefighters are very good dancers also. (6)Last year they put on "Bye-bye Birdie," and this year they will put on "The Music Man." (7)The musical will be presented on October 15th and 16th. (8)It will be in the auditorium at City Hall. (9)You can get more information by calling City Hall during the day.

1. Who
   What
   When
2. Why
   What
3. Who
   What
4. Who
   What
5. Who
6. Which
   When
7. When
8. Where
9. How

In this exercise you will ask questions to get information about events. When you hear or read about an event, you must get enough information to enable you to participate, or tell someone about the event or to know all that has happened during a past event. Read each paragraph. You will notice that each sentence in the paragraph is numbered. Each sentence is supposed to give a bit of information about the event. Following each paragraph is a list of numbers corresponding with the numbers of the sentences in the paragraph. For each of these items ask a question or questions which the sentence answers. The first word of each question is given

(1)It's almost time for "beach clean-up." (2)Each year, around the beginning of June everyone in our neighborhood goes out to clean up the beach. (3)We pick up trash and debris that have washed up onto the beach so that the beach will be nice and clean for the summer beach season. (4)The neighbors will meet Saturday morning at the Smiths' home between eight and nine o'clock so everyone can get a trash bag. (5)The filled trash bags should be left behind the benches on the beach.

1. What
2. When
   Who
3. What
   Why
4. Who
   When
   Where
   Why
5. What
   Where

---

(1)Last night there was a fire in our next-door neighbors' yard. (2)The firefighters think that someone threw a fire cracker into a trash can behind the house and the stuff inside caught fire. (3)It was about ten o'clock last night when my dad smelled smoke. (4)He looked all around our house and in the neighbors' yards. (5)He spotted something burning in our next-door neighbor's yard. (6)He called the fire department right away so the fire wouldn't spread. (7)The firefighters arrived about five minutes later. (8)The fire had started to spread to the porch. (9)There was some damage to the porch railing, but nothing else was harmed.

1. What
   When
2. How
   Who
3. When
   Who
   What
4. Where
5. What
   Where
   Who
6. Who
   Why
7. How long
8. Where
9. What

---

(1)Our principal will be interviewed on TV tonight. (2)He just won the governor's award for "Principal of the Year." (3)A reporter from Channel 7 came to our school today to talk to Mr. Grey, the principal. (4)The reporter told the students that the interview would be broadcast during the six o'clock news, near the end of the program. (5)Mr. Gray won the award because he made sure that everyone in our school did a special project and learned something extra. (6)Then, he learned about each project by inviting students in to his office into small groups and listening to what each one had learned about his or her special project. (7)He made each student in our school feel special by spending time with them and showing interest in the special projects.

1. Who
2. What
3. Who
   Where
   When
   Why
4. Who
   What
   When
5. Why
6. How
7. How

In the exercises on this page you will read about an event in which you will be asked to take part, or an event that occurred in the past. However, the information in each paragraph is not complete. You would be unable to take part in a future event or to accurately tell about a past event because you'd be missing some information. Refer to the question guide; make sure each of the questions can be answered giving you enough information. Also, note that some of the information included in some of the paragraphs might not be directly related to the message. After reading each paragraph ask the questions necessary to give you the information that you need.

1. Catherine said to tell you that there's going to be a surprise birthday party for Emma next Friday night. Try to get there before seven-thirty because Nancy's going to be arriving with Emma somewhere between seven-thirty and eight o'clock. It's Emma's birthday, and they're planning to get her a gift. She collects all kinds of little animal statues, so some of us are going to chip in and get her a cute little statue of a penguin. If you want to go in on that with us give the money to Tamara.

Do you have enough information to take part in this surprise party? What's missing?

2. The neighborhood meeting that was supposed to be Monday night at the Tompkins' house has been rescheduled. The Tompkins are going to California for six months, and so they could not have the meeting at their house. The meeting will be next Thursday night at eight o'clock. If you like, bring a snack because there'll be a little social gathering afterwards.

Do you have the information you need to go to the neighborhood meeting?

3. Frank called during his lunch hour and said that there's a sale on wheelbarrows today only. He said that you should bring the station wagon and the money and he'll meet you there and you can get the wheelbarrow and take it home.

Do you have enough information to meet Frank and buy the wheelbarrow? What's missing?

4. Vincent just called to tell me that the concert that was supposed to be on TV tonight won't be broadcast because of the president's speech. It's supposed to be on next Friday. Could you call and tell her so she can tell the others to be sure to look for it next Friday.

Do you have enough information to let people know about the change in the concert's broadcast time?

5. My Uncle, Jacob said he'd take us out on his fishing boat with him. Pack warm clothes and be prepared to spend the night on the island in case it looks like a storm might come. There's some food on the boat but we should probably bring some other things especially if we end up staying overnight. Also, could you bring your camera? I loaned mine to my brother and I haven't gotten it back yet. I'd love to get some pictures of us out on the boat. You'd better leave the phone number for your mom so she can get in touch with you if she needs to.

Do you have enough information to be ready to go out on your friend's uncle's boat and tell your parents about the plans? What else to you need to know?

In the exercises on this page you will read about an event in which you will be asked to take part, or an event that occurred in the past. However, the information in each paragraph is not complete. You would be unable to take part in a future event o to accurately tell about a past event because you'd be missing some information. Refer to the question guide; make sure each of the questions can be answered giving you enough information. Also, note that some of the information included in some of the paragraphs might not be directly related to the message. After reading each paragraph ask the questions necessary to give you the information that you need.

Question Guide	
What	Whose
Who	Which
When	How many
Where	How much
How	Why

1. Could you write an article about the fire for the school newspaper? Here's the information that I have. I hope you can use this to write your article. The fire happened last Wednesday. Some things in the room were burned and some things were okay. The firefighters came into the building at around eleven o'clock PM and stayed until they were sure the fire was out and would not start up again.

Do you have enough information to write an article about this fire for your school newspaper? What's missing?

2. It's going to be a great parade. Plan to come and tell your friends to come. The high school band will march and play some of the songs that they played at the band concert. There will be some antique cars in the parade. Some of the businesses in town will make floats. There will be places set up along the way to buy snacks and drinks.

Do you have enough information to plan to come to the parade and to invite your friends to the parade? What's missing?

3. Jim's class will graduate next Sunday. You are invited to the graduation ceremony, and afterwards there's a gathering on the lawn behind the school for families and friends of the graduates. After the activities at school there's going to be a party at Jim's house. Most of his family and friends will come to that party. Jim got some new black leather shoes to wear to the graduation. He's afraid his feet'll hurt because he hasn't had a chance to break the new shoes in and the graduates will have to stand for a long time during the ceremony.

Do you have enough information to plan to attend Jim's graduation? What's missing? Is there anything mentioned here that you *don't* need to know?

4. Mr. Judd is going to get an award from the Mayor. Anyone can come and watch him get the award. If you can't come you can see it on TV because a TV news crew will be at the meeting and will film the award ceremony. It would be nice if you could tell your parents and some of your neighbors about this so they can come and see him get this award.

Do you know all about Mr. Judd's award? Could you tell someone about this event to get him interested in coming? What's missing?

5. Bill told his neighbor, Mr. Walters, that there's going to be a big yard sale next Saturday. Everyone in the neighborhood should gather up stuff that they would like to sell and write down the prices that they think each thing is worth. The money that the neighbors get from selling everyone's stuff will be used to buy a basketball backboard and hoop to put at the end of the dead-end street.

Does Mr. Walters have enough information to take part in the neighborhood yard sale? What's missing?

Here is a list of events that **are going to happen**. Pretend like you know all about each one. Make up all the information using the question guide to help you remember to include all the important things that people should know. Then, tell this information to a partner. She should listen and determine whether or not she has enough information to take part in the event. If not, she should ask you questions until she does have enough information.

Question Guide	
What	Whose
Who	Which
When	How many
Where	How much
How	Why

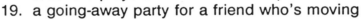

1. a surprise birthday party
2. a class picnic
3. a family reunion
4. a beach party
5. a camping trip
6. a car wash
7. a "pot luck" supper
8. a dog show
9. a craft fair
10. a sports banquet
11. a neighborhood baseball game
12. tryouts for parts in a play
13. going to see a play
14. a concert
15. the election of class or club officers
16. a clam-bake
17. an after-school computer class
18. a teacher/student basketball game (a team of teachers plays a team of students)
19. a going-away party for a friend who's moving
20. an awards ceremony
21. the showing of a special film
22. a school dance
23. kite-flying contest
24. a cookout
25. a hayride
26. a costume party
27. a fireworks display
28. a bake sale
29. a class trip to the art museum
30. a parade
31. a scavenger hunt
32. an important person coming to town to give a speech
33. a 10 kilometer road race
34. a karate match
35. planting a community garden
36. a bowling tournament
37. a recycling drive
38. a special luncheon for teachers at your school (prepared by the students)
39. Thanksgiving dinner
40. a barn raising

*Here is a list of events that **already happened**. Pretend like you know about each one. It's your job to tell everything you know about each event to someone who's going to write an article for a newspaper or give a news broadcast telling about the event. Make up all the information about each event and tell it to your partner (and pretend that he will write the article or broadcast the story). Use the question guide to make sure you include all important information. Have fun!*

Question Guide	
What	Whose
Who	Which
When	How many
Where	How much
How	Why

1. a parade honoring a town hero
2. a dog show
3. a fire in the neighborhood
4. the grand opening of a new grocery store
5. road construction (where the main street in town was torn up for a long time)
6. the high school soccer team's championship game
7. a cooking contest at the county fair
8. the time aliens landed in the shopping center parking lot
9. the christening of the town's new fire engine
10. a bad storm
11. a city worker discovered an alligator in the sewer downtown
12. when the town hospital finished building its new heliport
13. the air show that came to town
14. the town window-decorating contest
15. the time a kangaroo escaped from the zoo
16. a delivery-truck accident where the truck's contents spilled out onto the street
17. the day the president came to speak in our town
18. an election
19. a fashion show
20. a softball tournament
21. a big snowstorm
22. a display of rare jewels
23. a hot air balloon race
24. a 10 kilometer road race
25. a meteor shower

When you listen to explanations of how to do something you must get enough information. When someone explains how to do something it is his job to tell you exactly what things you need and what actions you must do, and in what order things must be done.

As a listener, it's your job to make sure you get the information you need–exactly what to do, exactly what things to use and in what sequence things must be done.

To the right is an explanation of how to change a flat tire. Each sentence is numbered. Each sentence tells of one step of the process of fixing a flat tire. The sentences occur in the right order, telling just what to to first, second, etc. Each sentence also includes the name of a particular object and tells exactly what to do.

1. Pry off the wheel cover of the damaged tire
2. Slightly loosen the lug nuts with a wrench
3. Make sure the emergency brake is engaged so the car remains in place.
4. Secure the wheel opposite the damaged tire in place by placing a rock in front of and behind this wheel.
5. Using the jack raise the car off the ground.
6. Loosen and remove the lug nuts from the wheel and studs
7. Remove the tire and wheel by sliding it off the studs
8. Place the new tire and wheel onto the studs
9. Install a lug nut onto each stud by hand
10. Tighten each lug nut just enough so that the wheel won't move
11. Lower the car to the ground
12. Remove the jack
13. Tighten the lug nuts securely using the wrench
14. Replace the wheel cover

Pretend that you're not quite sure of something about this explanation. You want to know exactly what to do in case you really do get a flat tire some day! Ask questions to clarify this procedure in your own mind.

Example:
how to get the wheel cover off the damaged tire
How do you get the wheel cover off?

1. how to remove the lug nuts
2. what to do so the car won't roll
3. how to make sure the car will remain in the right position
4. how to raise the car up off the ground
5. what to do before you remove the wheel with the damaged tire
6. how to remove the tire and wheel
7. what to do with the new tire and wheel
8. how to install the lug nuts on the new wheel
9. how much the lug nuts need to be tightened
10. how to position the car after the lug nuts are removed
11. when to remove the jack
12. what to do after you remove the jack

Questioning someone during a conversation

Sometimes when people speak they might say something that is not quite clear to you. Your partner might use an expression that you don't understand. The list of statements below will give you a chance to practice questioning exactly what a speaker means by a certain phrase.

In each of these statements an idiomatic expression is used and written in italics. Practice asking questions to clarify statements. Ask your partner what she meant by the phrases printed in italics in each of these sentences.

Example:
  Statement: I tried until I was *blue in the face.*
  Question: What do you mean by *blue in the face?*

1. I guess we'll have to *face the music* when mom comes home.
2. Our business is operating *in the red.*
3. It was good to see Richard and James *bury the hatchet.*
4. George *did a double take* when he saw my new hair color.
5. Bill tried to *pull the wool over Ken's eyes* when he explained the deal.
6. I wonder why Ron *gave me the cold shoulder* at the party.
7. Mr. Justin said that he had *a bone to pick* with my dad.
8. When I was in Tokyo last year I felt like *a fish out of water.*
9. Mom really *put her foot in her mouth* when she talked to that reporter.
10. Tell me what you mean, don't *beat around the bush.*
11. Uncle Jack *went into orbit* when Bob showed him the picture.
12. The teacher really *flew off the handle* when she saw how disrupted the class was.
13. Mark wanted to get *right to the point.* He said that he wanted to *talk turkey.*
14. My boss *looked daggers* at me when he saw me come in late this morning.
15. He really didn't mean to yell at you. He just needed to *let off steam.*
16. Bryan got tired of the teasing and told Kim to just *knock it off.*
17. I hope Jerry doesn't ride in my car. He's such a *back seat driver.*
18. Shelly opened a *can of worms* when she said she had news about the new contract.
19. That movie *cracked me up.*
20. I need to *brush up* on my algebra before I take the test.
21. John must have been feeling *in the pink* today judging by how well he did in that race.
22. What Tanya said sounded pretty *fishy* to me.
23. Looking for Benny will prove to be a *wild goose chase*, I'm sure.
24. Hank has a real *chip in his shoulder.*
25. Beth said that Tony was a *real heel.*

Try to figure out what's in these packages.
Your partner should pretend she knows what's
in each package, one at a time. Then try to
figure out what's in each one by asking
questions. Ask only the kinds of questions that
*can be answered **yes** or **no**.*

Look at the list of words, phrases or statements in the left-hand column. Each of these is the answer to one of the questions in the right hand column. Draw a line from each answer to the correct question.

1. a cocker spaniel
2. a peanut butter and jelly sandwich
3. a rose
4. a rubber band
5. about a half hour
6. because our dog is shedding
7. good and chocolaty
8. in his closet
9. in its shell
10. in the parking lot behind the building
11. it has calcium and that's good for your bones
12. July fourth
13. late in the summer
14. mix chocolate syrup in white milk
15. my fourth grade teacher
16. nine o'clock in the morning
17. peanuts
18. polish it
19. purple
20. six o'clock
21. so you won't get cavities
22. soldering pipes
23. the alarm clock will ring
24. the Lone Ranger
25. the police officer

1. Who rode a white horse named Silver?
2. What time does the evening news come on?
3. Where are Bill's cowboy boots?
4. What would you like for lunch?
5. Which flower is your favorite?
6. How long before dinner?
7. Why should I drink milk?
8. What should I use to hold these cards together?
9. What can I do to make this silver tray shine?
10. Who arrested the burglar?
11. How do you make chocolate milk?
12. Where does a turtle live?
13. How does the cake taste?
14. When will the tomatoes be ripe?
15. Where should we park?
16. Who taught you to do long division problems?
17. Why should I brush my teeth?
18. What color is a girraffe's tongue?
19. Why is there so much white fur all over your house?
20. What does a plumber use a blowtorch for?
21. How will I know when to get up?
22. What kind of dog is that?
23. What is peanut butter made of?
24. What time does the store open?
25. When is American Independence Day celebrated?

Look at the list of words, phrases or statements in the left-hand column. Each of these is the answer to one of the questions in the right hand column. Draw a line from each answer to the correct question.

1. Vasco Nunez de Balboa
2. because it would harm them if they swallowed it
3. by replacing the pipe with a hole in it
4. eight
5. French, oil and vinegar, ranch, and creamy Italian
6. in my back pack
7. to make it sweet
8. because she had to study for a test on Monday
9. late enough that there's no longer a chance of frost and very cold temperatures
10. my friends gave me a surprise party and we all had a great time
11. in northern Arizona
12. probably on the floor in her closet
13. read the washing instructions
14. because smoke from cigarettes can cause people to get sick
15. so they won't get rabies
16. Texas, Arizona, and California
17. because Uncle Dave was telling jokes
18. to protect them from breathing the smoke
19. twenty dollars
20. whenever the soil gets dried out

1. Where do you carry your trail mix when you go hiking?
2. Why did Gloria leave the party early on Sunday?
3. What do you remember about your eleventh birthday?
4. When should I water the plant?
5. Why do people use sugar in their coffee?
6. Who discovered the Pacific Ocean?
7. Why do dogs get rabies shots?
8. How many pints are in a gallon?
9. Where is the Grand Canyon?
10. Which states in the US border on Mexico?
11. What should you do before you launder a new shirt?
12. Why should you keep medicine out of the reach of children?
13. What kind of salad dressings do you have?
14. How did the plumber stop the leak?
15. Why can't people smoke in airplanes?
16. Why do the firefighters wear breathing masks when they go into the burning building?
17. When should I plant the vegetables in my garden?
18. Where did Dianna put her ice skates?
19. Why was everyone laughing?
20. How much did that watch cost?

111

Pretend like you're a TV talk show host. Your job is to interview famous people. You should ask questions leading your special guests to talk about things that would interest the audience. For example, people would probably be interested in:

1. where the famous person grew up
2. what he did to learn to do the things that he or she is famous for
3. who some special people in her life are
4. where he is living now
5. where he has traveled
6. what he liked about some of these places
7. when she first became interested in her special career
8. just what it is that he is best known for
9. other things that she has done that she is proud of
10. his family
11. his favorite books, movies, TV shows
12. her hobbies
13. where she likes to go on vacation
14. what some of the special times or events in his career
15. what kinds of things she might plan to do in the future

Here are some ideas of some famous people who might be interviewed on your TV show. Use your imagination! Take turns with a partner being the interviewer and the famous person. Ask and answer questions that would interest an audience.

1. a scientist who made an amazing discovery
2. a famous chef
3. the mayor of your town
4. the president
5. an astronaut who walked on another planet
6. a doctor who can perform life-saving operations
7. a famous artist
8. a rock star
9. an movie actor
10. an author of books that you like to read
11. Miss America
12. the winner of a great sailing contest
13. the MVP of the team that won the world series
14. a long distance truck driver
15. chief of staff of the U.S. Armed Forces
16. the New York City Chief of Police
17. the leader of the United Nations
18. an engineer or architect who designed a special bridge
19. director of the Humane Society of the U.S., an organization protecting animals from cruelty
20. a rocket scientist
21. Surgeon General of the United States
22. a cartoon character who came to life for a day

Below is a map of the continental United States which shows states and their respective time zones. Pretend like you want to know what time it is in one time zone when it's a different time in a different time zone. Use the information below to develop questions. Your partner should answer your questions. You want to know what time it is in:

Example:
What time is it in New York City when it's 12:00 P.M. in San Diego, California?

It's 9:00 P.M. in New York City.

1. Seattle, Washington when it's 3:00 A.M. in Raleigh, North Carolina
2. Tulsa, Oklahoma when it's 1:00 P.M. in Los Angeles, California
3. Denver, Colorado when it's 2:00 A.M. in New York, New York
4. Pittsburgh Pennsylvania when it's 6:00 P.M. in DeMoines, Iowa
5. Salt Lake City, Utah when it's 11:00 A.M. in Wheeling, West Virginia
6. Savennah, Georgia when it's 4:00 P.M. in San Francisco, California
7. Arlington, Virginia when it's 2:00 P.M. in Detroit, Michigan
8. Phoenix, Arizona when it's 8:00 P.M. in Cleveland, Ohio
9. Wichita, Kansas when it's 5:00 A.M. in Santa Fe, New Mexico
10. Shrevsport, Louisiana when it's 7:00 P.M. in Miami, Florida
11. Deluth, Minnesota when it's 12:00 A.M. in Boston, Massachusetts
12. Billings, Montana when it's 11:00 A.M. in Lansing, Michigan
13. Burlington, Vermont when it's 3:00 P.M. in Dallas, Texas
14. Greenville, South Carolina when it's 10:00 A.M. in Portland, Maine
15. Little Rock, Arkansas when it's 9:00 A.M. in Arlington, Virginia
16. Providence, Rhode Island when it's 1:00 A.M. in Portland, Oregon

Pacific Time   Mountain Time   Central Time   Eastern Time